Contents

About This Series

by Edward Zlotkowski

The following volume, *Projects That Matter: Concepts and Models for Service-Learning in Engineering,* represents the 14th in a series of monographs on service-learning and academic disciplinary areas. Ever since the early 1990s, educators interested in reconnecting higher education not only with neighboring communities but also with the American tradition of education for service have recognized the critical importance of winning faculty support for this work. Faculty, however, tend to define themselves and their responsibilities largely in terms of the academic disciplines/disciplinary areas in which they have been trained. Hence, the logic of the present series.

The idea for this series first surfaced late in 1994 at a meeting convened by Campus Compact to explore the feasibility of developing a national network of service-learning educators. At that meeting, it quickly became clear that some of those assembled saw the primary value of such a network in its ability to provide concrete resources to faculty working in or wishing to explore service-learning. Out of that meeting there developed, under the auspices of Campus Compact, a new national group of educators called the Invisible College, and it was within the Invisible College that the monograph project was first conceived. Indeed, a review of both the editors and contributors responsible for many of the volumes in this series would reveal significant representation by faculty associated with the Invisible College.

If Campus Compact helped supply the initial financial backing and impulse for the Invisible College and for this series, it was the American Association for Higher Education (AAHE) that made completion of the project feasible. Thanks to its reputation for innovative work, AAHE was not only able to obtain the funding needed to support the project up through actual publication, it was also able to assist in attracting many of the teacher-scholars who participated as writers and editors. AAHE is grateful to the Corporation for National Service–Learn and Serve America for its financial support of the series.

Three individuals in particular deserve to be singled out for their contributions. Sandra Enos, former Campus Compact project director for Integrating Service With Academic Study, was shepherd to the Invisible College project. John Wallace, professor of philosophy at the University of Minnesota, was the driving force behind the creation of the Invisible College. Without his vision and faith in the possibility of such an undertaking, assembling the human resources needed for this series would have been very difficult. Third, AAHE's endorsement — and all that followed in its wake

— was due largely to then AAHE vice president Lou Albert. Lou's enthusiasm for the monograph project and his determination to see it adequately supported have been critical to its success. It is to Sandra, John, and Lou that the monograph series as a whole must be dedicated.

Another individual to whom the series owes a special note of thanks is Teresa E. Antonucci, who, as program manager for AAHE's Service-Learning Project, has helped facilitate much of the communication that has allowed the project to move forward.

The Rationale Behind the Series

A few words should be said at this point about the makeup of both the general series and the individual volumes. Although engineering may seem an unusual choice of discipline with which to link service-learning, focused as it is on highly technical questions of design and structure, "natural fit" has not, in fact, been a determinant factor in deciding which disciplines/interdisciplinary areas the series should include. Far more important have been considerations related to the overall range of disciplines represented. Since experience has shown that there is probably no disciplinary area — from architecture to zoology — where service-learning cannot be fruitfully employed to strengthen students' abilities to become active learners as well as responsible citizens, a primary goal in putting the series together has been to demonstrate this fact. Thus, some rather natural choices for inclusion — disciplines such as anthropology, geography, and religious studies — have been passed over in favor of other, sometimes less obvious selections from business, science, and technology as well as several important interdisciplinary areas. Should the present series of volumes prove useful and well received, we can then consider filling in the many gaps we have left this first time around.

If a concern for variety has helped shape the series as a whole, a concern for legitimacy has been central to the design of the individual volumes. To this end, each volume has been both written by and aimed primarily at academics working in a particular disciplinary/interdisciplinary area. Many individual volumes have, in fact, been produced with the encouragement and active support of relevant discipline-specific national societies.

Furthermore, each volume has been designed to include its own appropriate theoretical, pedagogical, and bibliographical material. Especially with regard to theoretical and bibliographical material, this design has resulted in considerable variation both in quantity and in level of discourse. Thus, for example, a volume such as Accounting contains more introductory and less bibliographical material than does Composition — simply because there is less written on and less familiarity with service-learning in accounting.

However, no volume is meant to provide an extended introduction to service-learning *as a generic concept*. For material of this nature, the reader is referred to such texts as Kendall's *Combining Service and Learning: A Resource Book for Community and Public Service* (NSIEE 1990) and Jacoby's *Service-Learning in Higher Education* (Jossey-Bass 1996).

I would like to conclude with a note of special thanks to the volume's editor, Edmund Tsang, whose dedication to a vision of socially responsive engineering deserves the gratitude not only of his engineering colleagues but also of the communities that benefit from their enlightened expertise.

March 2000

Introduction

by Edmund Tsang

Most engineering educators appreciate the value of experiential education where students learn through the experience of applying the theoretical knowledge and skills they have gained in the classroom. These educators realize that the more like the real world the learning environment is, the more students learn in depth and in breadth.

Experiential education takes many forms in the undergraduate engineering curriculum: They range from formal internship/cooperative experiences to undergraduate research experiences, project-based coursework, laboratory experiences, and field trips. With such a cornucopia of pedagogies already available to engineering faculty, does service-learning deserve serious consideration as engineering faculty members ponder the question of how best to prepare engineering undergraduates for the 21st century; in particular, how to help them meet the performance outcomes described in *Engineering Criteria 2000* (ABET 1998)?

Engineering Education for the 21st Century

A paradigm shift is taking place in undergraduate engineering education, with the inclusion in the curriculum of the objective of helping students develop what some have called "softer skills." Citing the end of the Cold War, a global economy, and information technology, a joint report of the Engineering Deans Council and the Corporate Roundtable of the American Society for Engineering Education (1994) asks engineering educators to "reexamine their curricula and programs to ensure they prepare students for the broadened world of engineering work" (5). That Green Report, *Engineering Education for a Changing World,* also asks colleges of engineering to accelerate implementing programs that help engineering undergraduates develop these softer skills to meet the challenges of the 21st century. They include team skills such as collaborative active learning; communication skills; leadership; an understanding and appreciation of the diversity of students, faculty, and staff; an appreciation of different cultures and business practices; the understanding that the practice of engineering is now global; and understanding of the societal, economic, and environmental impacts of engineering decisions. The importance of these softer skills is also stressed in a 1996 National Science Foundation report that identifies them as "ancillary" to the success of future SMET (science, mathematics, engineering, and technology) graduates.

Engineering Criteria 2000 (ABET 1998), the accreditation criteria established by the Accreditation Board for Engineering and Technology (ABET), formalize the incorporation of these softer skills into the undergraduate curriculum. The criteria require engineering programs to demonstrate that their graduates have, among other competencies, an ability to function on multidisciplinary teams; an understanding of professional and ethical responsibility; an ability to communicate effectively; the broad education necessary to understand the impact of engineering solutions in a global and societal context; and a knowledge of contemporary issues.

The next few sections of this introduction define service-learning and present some arguments for its integration into the engineering curriculum as one important strategy for educating undergraduates to meet the societal needs and challenges of the 21st century.

What Is Service-Learning?

Although service-learning has received relatively little attention in the engineering disciplines, it has been well established in the social sciences, and in disciplines in which clinical experience represents an important part of the learning process.[1] A large-scale study by A.W. Astin and L.J. Sax (1998) of the impact that participation in community service projects has on undergraduate student development has shown that such participation substantially enhances a student's academic learning, life-skill development, and sense of civic responsibility. In engineering, service-learning has the potential to help students gain the skills necessary for lifelong learning and for practicing engineering in a manner cognizant of professional and civic responsibilities.

A primer on service-learning edited by B. Jacoby and Associates (1996) defines this pedagogy as "a form of experiential education in which students engage in activities that address human and community needs together with structured opportunities intentionally designed to promote student learning and development. Reflection and reciprocity are key concepts of service-learning" (5).

The importance of reflection is rooted in the fact that

> *learning and development do not necessarily occur as a result of experience itself but as a result of a reflective component explicitly designed to foster learning and development. Reflection should include opportunities for participants to receive feedback from those persons being served, as well as from peers and program leaders. (6)*

In service-learning, the goal of reflection is "to promote learning about the larger social issues behind the needs to which [student] service is responding. This learning includes a deeper understanding of the historical, sociological, cultural, economic, and political contexts of the needs or issues being addressed" (7).

As for reciprocity, it implies a new, more equal approach to academy-community partnering:

> *[T]he needs of the community, as determined by its members, define what the service tasks will be. Service-learning avoids placing students into community settings based solely on desired student learning outcomes and providing services that do not meet actual needs or perpetuate a state of need rather than seeking and addressing the causes of need. Through reciprocity, students develop a greater sense of belonging and responsibility as members of a larger community. Community members being served learn how to take responsibility for their own needs and become empowered to develop mechanisms and relationships to address them. (7)*

Neither of these concepts, however, should be seen as in any way compromising the academic seriousness of the service undertaking. According to J. Howard (1993), editor of the peer-reviewed *Michigan Journal of Community Service Learning*, service-learning also should embody 10 best practices:

1. Academic credit is for learning, not for service;
2. Do not compromise academic rigor;
3. Set learning goals for students;
4. Establish criteria for the selection of community service placements;
5. Provide educationally sound mechanisms to harvest the community learning;
6. Provide supports for students to learn how to harvest the community learning;
7. Minimize the distinction between students' community learning role and the classroom learning role;
8. Rethink the faculty instructional role;
9. Be prepared for uncertainty and variation in student learning outcomes; and
10. Maximize the community responsibility orientation of the course. (3-7)

Building on these suggestions, we can identify four steps as essential to service-learning projects in engineering (Tsang, Martin, and Decker 1997). Faculty must:

1. Identify a community need that matches course learning objectives; form a partnership;
2. Create and implement a solution;
3. Evaluate that solution for continuous improvement; and
4. Engage students in structured reflection. (1)

Why Service-Learning?

Any definition of engineering would include "service to society" or "meeting societal needs" as a goal of the profession. In the 21st century, the challenges engineers face in using technology to meet societal needs and human aspirations are substantial. The more obvious domestic needs include

- rebuilding a decaying urban infrastructure;
- developing sustainable development;
- improving K-12 education, particularly mathematics, science, and technology instruction; and
- fighting pollution that impacts more heavily on those in the lower socioeconomic class.

As a result of the devolution of power from the federal to the state and municipal governments, local communities are increasingly called on to address these needs themselves, despite their lack of expertise and resources. Meanwhile, on a global level, other fundamental needs call out for attention. These include

- supplying food, clean water and air, and energy for an increasing world population;
- protecting ecosystems; and
- fighting pollution that transcends national boundaries.

As society attempts to meet these and other needs during the coming decades, the contribution of engineers cannot be underestimated — not just because of the special knowledge and skills they bring to the problem-solving process. As C.P. Snow noted in his famous essay "The Two Cultures" (1956), scientists, and by inference engineers, possess a special kind of moral authority:

> *But the greatest enrichment the scientific culture could give us is — though it does not originate like that — a moral one. Among scientists, deep-natured men know, as starkly as any men have known, that the individual human condition is tragic; for all its triumphs and joys, the essence of it is loneliness and the end death. But what they will not admit is that because the individual condition is tragic, therefore the social condition must be tragic, too. Because a man must die, that is no excuse for his dying before his time and after a servile life. The impulse behind the scientists drives them to limit the area of tragedy, to take nothing as tragic that can conceivably lie within men's will. . . . It is that kind of moral health of the scientists which, in the last few years, the rest of us have needed most; and of which, because the two cultures scarcely touch, we have been most deprived.* (414)

But future engineers will need more than technical knowledge and skills to assume the moral leadership required to meet the challenges of the 21st century. Because solutions to many societal problems require extensive interaction and communication with people of diverse social, cultural, and economic backgrounds, the engineer of the future will also have to have, in the words of *Engineering Criteria 2000*, "an ability to communicate effectively" and "an ability to function on multidisciplinary teams."

Thus the challenge facing engineering education today revolves around the development of pedagogical approaches not limited to the inculcation of technical knowledge and skills. The Green Report of ASEE (1994) clearly states that "with technology playing a growing role in both professional and public policy decisions, it is important that engineers are prepared to participate actively in decision-making processes" (1). This, in turn, implies that engineers will need to be sensitive to the power relationships inherent in the implementation of technological solutions (for example, who pays and who gains), and have empathy with those groups potentially affected in a negative way by technological decisions. Thus, *Engineering Criteria 2000* requires engineering programs to demonstrate that their graduates have "the broad education necessary to understand the impact of engineering solutions in a global and societal context," "a knowledge of contemporary issues," and "an understanding of professional and ethical responsibility" (ABET 1998).

It is in meeting the learning objectives in educating engineering undergraduates for the 21st century — those described in *Engineering Criteria 2000* — that service-learning distinguishes itself from other forms of experiential education. By engaging in thoughtfully organized "activities that address human and community needs together with structured opportunities intentionally designed to promote student learning and development" (Jacoby 1996: 5), engineering students have an opportunity to interact with highly diverse populations and so can better develop their abilities "to function on multidisciplinary teams" and "to communicate effectively" (ABET 1998). Through reflecting on the service experience they can develop "a deeper understanding of the historical, sociological, cultural, economic, and political contexts of the needs or issues being addressed" (Jacoby 1996: 7) and learn to appreciate "broad education necessary to understand the impact of engineering solutions in a global and societal context" (ABET 1998). Furthermore, by respecting the reciprocity central to service-learning — a reciprocity that ensures that "the needs of the community, as determined by its members, define what the service tasks will be" — they will "develop a greater sense of belonging and responsibility as members of a larger community" (Jacoby 1996: 7) and "an understanding of professional and ethical responsibility" (ABET 1998).

Nor should we underestimate the faculty appeal of such multidimensional education. According to the late Ernest L. Boyer (1990), many faculty "are drawn to [higher education] precisely because of their love for teaching or for service — even for making the world a better place" (xii). For such faculty, with their commitment to helping their students develop a sense of community and citizenship, service-learning can serve as an especially effective pedagogy.

Finally, it seems clear that society too will gain considerably if more engineering faculty begin to integrate service projects into their course designs, since so many societal problems require the kind of special knowledge and skill engineers possess. Faculty who sponsor such projects can be said to engage in what Peters, Jordan, and Lemme (1999) have called "public science" — or, in this case, "public engineering" — "a form of public scholarship [that] calls on scientists to enter into partnerships with citizens from other professions or sectors in work that closely links knowledge creation with public problem solving and policy-making" (34).

"At no time in our history has the need been greater for connecting the work of the academy to the social and environmental challenges beyond the campus," Boyer wrote in *Scholarship Reconsidered* (1990: xii). Service-learning answers this need by connecting student learning with the real-world challenges of the local societal environment. In doing so, it explicitly answers the ASEE Green Report's (1994) call for broadening the community base that engineering colleges reach out to: "A key element in the success of these efforts [engineering education in a changing world] will be partnerships: partnerships not only with industry, but with K-12 schools, community colleges, the broader university community, government, and among engineering colleges" (3).

Volume Contents

The purpose of this monograph is not only to serve as a practical guide for faculty seeking to integrate service-learning into an engineering course but also to examine larger issues of engineering education, the mission of higher education in an increasingly technologically oriented society, and the role of service-learning as a catalysis for program reform and educational enhancement. As contributions to a volume in the American Association for Higher Education's Series on Service-Learning in the Disciplines, the essays in this monograph have been selected because of both their authors' experience in using service-learning and their relevance to issues of concern to engineering educators.

Compared with the others in the AAHE series, this volume reflects less emphasis on service-learning theory — in part because service-learning in engineering is still relatively new and in part because of the temperament and professional training of the engineering contributors. As one reviewer put it during the peer-review phase of putting the volume together: "The audience for this monograph is the engineering education community — that community will expect practical applications of the theory that will lead to improved engineering education." Nevertheless, though each contributing author makes the case for service-learning explicitly in its potential to meet specific performance outcomes identified in *Engineering Criteria 2000*, implicitly the contributors, individually and collectively, raise questions that go to the heart of engineering education and the role of institutions of higher education.

The volume is organized into three parts. Part I deals with larger issues of integrating and sustaining service-learning in engineering. Part II provides detailed case studies of service-learning courses and reflections by their instructors. Part III makes available additional resources of value to engineering faculty wishing to adapt and implement service-learning.

Gerald Eisman opens the first essay of Part I with a quotation that reminds us of questions often raised by faculty members in the humanities about the higher purposes of a university education: "There is one quality more important than 'know-how.' . . . This is 'know-what' by which we determine not only how to accomplish our purposes, but what our purposes are to be." Eisman answers questions related to "know-what" by asserting that "as educators of future technology specialists, we must concern ourselves with the preparation of students who fully understand the broad impact of technology on our communities." Eisman then gives a personal account of his work with students in designing information systems for community partners in the San Francisco Bay area, thereby making the case that service-learning

> *offer[s] opportunities to prepare students for the actual work of applying technology to the "human" problems of the real world while providing significant lessons in the skills and knowledge required of a technology professional. Thus, properly implemented, these teaching methodologies can add to discipline-specific learning without taking anything away.*

It should be noted that the volume makes no attempt to hide the challenges and obstacles involved in successfully integrating and institutionalizing service-learning as an agent for educational reform. In Part I's second essay, I myself identify several challenges and obstacles common to this work — challenges related to issues such as scheduling, the "professional" level of services provided by the students, and liability. This essay also looks at the difference between service-learning design projects and the kinds of community-based design projects commonly found in undergraduate engineering programs. I argue that the difference — which rests in the reflective component of service-learning — makes service-learning particularly valuable in addressing such *EC 2000* outcomes as "understand[ing] the impact of engineering solutions in a global and societal context" and "understanding . . . professional and ethical responsibility." In other words, because of the training, temperament, and preferences that characterize engineering methods of inquiry, the reflection service-learning entails represents both a major challenge and a special benefit.

This challenge is explicitly addressed by Jennifer Moffat and Rand Decker in the following essay, which offers a faculty guide to conducting service-learning reflection in engineering. The authors suggest that "becoming aware of one's own reflection experiences and recognizing the reflection techniques already present in one's routine" can serve as a foundation for "experiences to draw on while engaging students in service-learning reflection." They also offer concrete examples of service-learning reflection activities and tools.

The next essay in Part I, by Peter T. Martin and James Coles, discusses the institutional challenges that sustaining service-learning entails. The authors raise issues such as the faculty reward structure and faculty mentoring, and offer a workable way to proceed with criteria for evaluating faculty members engaged in service-learning as well as a mentoring guide for faculty members new to service-learning. The authors also contrast the subject-based learning inherent in the traditional lecture-format course with the problem-based learning favored by service-learning, and offer suggestions about the instructor's role in a problem-based learning environment. The essay includes a step-by-step plan for institutionalizing service-learning at both the departmental and the college levels.

Part I concludes with an essay by Rand Decker that addresses the "know-what" question raised in the first essay of Part I. Its author notes:

> *One of the many desired end products of service-learning is a population of socially aware professionals who will set aside a portion of their practice to meet recognized community needs; that is, engage in acts of professional activism.*

Decker sees "professional activism" as one effective way to address

> *a shift away from public sector entitlements as the dominant mechanism for meeting our society's civic responsibilities . . . [and] filling the resulting void with an institutionalized, private sector response is one of the only alternatives we have.*

Decker proposes a model for implementing professional activism that involves campus-based community service centers, local chapters of professional engineers' associations, and community service organizations. Together they can address "the epidemic disconnect between universities, their communities, and their alumni."

Part II consists of seven essays that offer detailed case studies of integrating service-learning in a wide range of courses commonly found in engineering programs. Several common threads run through these essays so they can also serve as a practical guide to engineering faculty members interested in implementing service-learning. Each contributing author describes how one can identify appropriate community partners and match community needs to course learning objectives; provides detailed information about his or her course(s) and its service-learning objectives and projects; describes methods for student assessment; and presents assessment results. But each author in Part II also makes a distinctive contribution to the pedagogy of service-learning in engineering by offering his or her unique observations and perspective as an experienced service-learning practitioner.

Edward J. Coyle and Leah H. Jamieson of Purdue University begin Part II with an essay describing their institution's Engineering Projects in Community Service (EPICS). The uniqueness of EPICS lies in the vertical integration of the design team and projects that are both multidisciplinary and capable of providing long-term design experience. The transportability of EPICS is demonstrated in the fact that other engineering programs have successfully adopted it; e.g., Notre Dame University and Iowa State University.

In the next essay, John Duffy describes how he integrates service-learning into seven courses at the undergraduate and graduate levels in a solar-energy program in mechanical engineering with projects varying from mandatory to elective, from 10 percent to 100 percent of the course grade. Although a capstone design course may seem like the logical place to incorporate service-learning, Duffy's essay has much to offer to faculty in demonstrating how service-learning can be incorporated into any upper-division lab course that has, as one of its learning objectives, uncertainty analysis involving field measurements or that includes selection of sensors, design of experiment, or hypothesis testing intended to teach students "how to perform field measurements in a 'messy' environment and how to estimate the accuracy of their results."

In his essay, Duffy also addresses the question: "Should service-learning projects be mandatory or elective?" and reviews the current literature on this debate. Finally, toward the end of his essay, he takes a measure of service-learning's potential impact in suggesting that

> *It is perhaps unrealistic to expect that basic attitudes toward the causes and solutions to societal problems would change after one relatively small project. Indeed, one could infer from these results that several courses with service-learning projects are needed to bring about significant, consistent changes in attitudes.*

C. Dianne Martin describes in her essay how service-learning and social impact analysis can be combined to address the recent emphasis on the ethical and social impact of computer technology. As a result of their service-learning projects, students

> *were able to relate the abstract social impact and ethical issues studied in the course to real-world sites. The students had to devise data-collection strategies that were not obtrusive or overly time-consuming for the sites involved. They had to be sensitive to the dignity and privacy of their clients.*

Martin cites scheduling as one difficulty in implementing service-learning projects, and admits that finding client sites for SIA projects was time-consuming. She suggests that this type of project "is best done with small classes (fewer than 30 students) or in a team-teach environment."

Course-specific essays contributed by me and by Marybeth Lima describe the integration of service-learning into first-year engineering design courses in mechanical engineering and biological engineering, respectively. Lima notes that

> *[W]hile interactive, student-centered learning opportunities are valid and available via industry-sponsored projects, completing a community service project is critical for developing civic awareness and social responsibility, two elements that are often overlooked in engineering education. Emphasizing the social component of engineering may enhance the attractiveness of the engineering discipline, particularly for women and minorities.*

According to Lima, in a world that is increasingly dependent on technology,

> *engineering must address social issues and fully interface with society in order to be a vital, positive influence. . . . The narrow focus on technical aspects of problem solving and the accompanying "conquer nature" paradigm have created other problems. . . . [Instead, we must embrace] social engineering as solving problems and/or achieving goals in the context of society while neutrally or positively affecting the planet and its inhabitants. This dimension must be considered in the engineering discipline if we are to avoid the dire consequences that will occur as a result of our currently narrow focus.*

Regarding student assessment, I argue in my essay that much can be learned using a qualitative approach rather than a quantitative approach (e.g., pre- and postservice surveys based on Likert-like scales) to measure the impact of service-learning on student development. I also identify several obstacles and challenges to partnering with K-12 teachers that have arisen in a service-learning course I offer in which first-year engineering students design and produce hardware and software to meet the instructional needs and specifications of K-12 teacher-clients. I recommend that engineering instructors "meet with teacher-partners prior to the actual course in order to . . . ensure that the teachers' classroom needs really do accommodate the course's learning objectives. Sometimes the needs of the teacher-partners can be better met by a 'technician' than an 'engineer.'" I also discuss the objection and challenge to service-learning offered by a philosophically very conservative student.

Next, Peter T. Martin describes the integration of service-learning into five courses focused on transportation, water, and environmental engineering. Thanks to the particular nature of civil and environmental engineering, Martin argues, service-learning effectively introduces engineering students to the fact

> *that the promotion and selection of an infrastructure project has a political dimension from the outset. More important, they learn that as engineers, they have a responsibility to contribute to the political process. They learn that engineers who abrogate this component of their professional responsibility diminish their leadership status, reducing their role to simply providing technical support. . . . Students learn about the political power of neighborhood councils, activist groups, and city council members and why these groups may influence decisions more than city engineers. They learn about citizenship, but not from a class called Citizenship.*

The first six cases presented in Part II emphasize the engineer-client aspect of the service-learning project, whereas the program described by David Vader and his colleagues emphasizes the use of service-learning to teach students in such a way that "their professional character and conduct are consistent with Christian faith commitments." These authors answer the larger question of "know-what" in engineering education from the perspective of a faith-based institution as they describe the role of service-learning in developing "responsible engineering." In doing so, they ask:

> *Is technique the principal responsibility of engineers, the material working out of objectives defined and supplied by others? Or are engineers also responsible, in view of our special knowledge, to create and use technologies in ways that preserve, honor, and advance prevailing social, political, and economic values?*

Part III of the volume provides additional resources to support faculty members learning about service-learning, and consists of two essays and a bibliography. Richard Ciocci describes the experience of integrating service-learning in a community college setting, whereas Susan Lord summarizes her thoughts on implementing service-learning for the first time. The volume concludes with a short, annotated bibliography in which the selected items possess the virtue either of being easy to use or effectively addressing how to prepare engineering undergraduates for the changing world of the 21st century, or of being inspirational.

Note

1. Private communication with Campus Compact staff. In a Campus Compact 1998 survey, 11,800 service-learning courses were reported by 575 member campuses.

References

Accreditation Board for Engineering and Technology. (1998). *Engineering Criteria 2000.* Available at the ABET website at <http://www.abet.org>.

American Society for Engineering Education. (1994). *Engineering Education for a Changing World.* A joint project report of the Engineering Deans Council and the Corporate Roundtable of the ASEE. Available at the ASEE website at <http://www.asee.org>.

Astin, A.W., and L.J. Sax. (1998). "How Undergraduates Are Affected by Service Participation." *Journal of College Student Development* 39(3): 251-263.

Boyer, E.L. (1990). *Scholarship Reconsidered: Priorities of the Professoriate.* Princeton, NJ: The Carnegie Foundation for the Advancement of Teaching.

Howard, J., ed. (1993). *Praxis I: A Faculty Casebook on Community Service Learning.* Ann Arbor, MI: OCSL Press.

Jacoby, B. (1996). "Service-Learning in Today's Higher Education." In *Service-Learning in Higher Education: Concepts and Practices,* edited by B. Jacoby and Associates, pp. 3-25. San Francisco, CA: Jossey-Bass.

Jacoby, B., and Associates, eds. (1996). *Service-Learning in Higher Education: Concepts and Practices.* San Francisco, CA: Jossey-Bass.

National Science Foundation. (1996). "Shaping the Future: New Expectations for Undergraduate Education in Science, Mathematics, Engineering, and Technology." Report available at the NSF website at <http://www.nsf.gov>.

Peters, S., N. Jordan, and G. Lemme. (1999). "Toward a Public Science: Building a New Social Contract Between Science and Society." In *Higher Education Exchange,* edited by Deborah Witte and David W. Brown, pp. 34-47. Dayton, OH: Kettering Foundation.

Snow, C.P. (Oct. 6, 1956). "The Two Cultures." *The New Statesman* 52: 413-414.

Tsang, E., C.D. Martin, and R. Decker. (1997). "Service-Learning as a Strategy for Engineering Education for the 21st Century." In *Proceedings of the 1997 American Society for Engineering Education Annual Conference, Milwaukee, WI, June 23-26, 1997.* CD-Rom.

What I Never Learned in Class:
Lessons From Community-Based Learning

by Gerald S. Eisman

> *There is one quality more important than "know-how.". . . This is "know-what" by which we determine not only how to accomplish our purposes, but what our purposes are to be.*
>
> — Norbert Wiener (1954: 250)

Back when my generation learned to program, and Norbert Wiener and others were developing the foundations of cybernetics, few had the foresight to envision a future where information technology would be central to daily life. We studied computer science and engineering with the expectation that the systems we worked on would primarily serve corporate and military clients. Look at what has occurred, however. The information technology revolution has made information systems central to all areas of our lives. As educators of future technology specialists, we must concern ourselves with preparing students who fully understand the broad impact of technology on our communities.

Most faculty in technology disciplines would agree with the importance of this preparation, but there is great disagreement on how the technology curricula can be modified to incorporate lessons in social impact. On the one hand, professional societies and accreditation agencies are calling for the inclusion of coursework in ethical considerations and the social implications of these disciplines. On the other, the general attitude of technology faculty is that these questions are important but should be raised somewhere else in the college curriculum.

In this essay, I will make the case that the pedagogies of community-based learning and service-learning offer opportunities to prepare students for the actual work of applying technology to the "human" problems of the real world while providing significant lessons in the skills and knowledge required of a technology professional. Thus, properly implemented, these teaching methodologies can add to discipline-specific learning without taking anything away. I will make this case with two examples of information system design projects that I worked on with my students in the San Francisco Bay area. In these endeavors we learned a lot about the interaction between technological systems and the people who would use them. It is my contention that our students — the future specialists responsible for designing and developing such systems — will be best served by having academic experiences that introduce them to the complexities of applying technology to community life.

The Case for Modifying the Curriculum

A growing body of literature justifies the inclusion of community-based and service-learning in technical disciplines such as computer science and engineering. This literature takes a variety of approaches, with most focusing on the moral imperative of preparing computing professionals to be aware of the ethical and social impact of their actions. Here are representative examples.

The We-Must-Avoid-the-Division-of-Society-Into-the-Haves-vs.-Have-Nots Argument: Perhaps this argument is best justified through reference to U.S. government studies on technology distribution. In 1997, the National Telecommunications and Information Administration (NTIA) updated its report on the "digital divide," the great disparity in use of the information technology infrastructure by various ethnic and income groups. In "Falling Through the Net II" (1997) the NTIA reports:

> *Despite [a] significant growth in computer ownership and usage overall, the growth has occurred to a greater extent within some income levels, demographic groups, and geographic areas, than in others. In fact, the "digital divide" between certain groups of Americans has increased between 1994 and 1997 so that there is now an even greater disparity in penetration levels among some groups. There is a widening gap, for example, between those at upper and lower income levels. Additionally, even though all racial groups now own more computers than they did in 1994, Blacks and Hispanics now lag even further behind Whites in their levels of PC-ownership and on-line access.*

The We-Must-Prepare-Students-to-Adopt-a-Code-of-Professional-Ethics Argument: A collection of professional society codes of ethics can be found at the website of the Online Ethics Center for Science and Engineering <http://ethics.cwru.edu>. Among these we find the following:

The Association of Computing Machinery (ACM) Council adopted its Code of Ethics and Professional Conduct in 1992. Section 1 of the code speaks to "general moral imperatives" that all ACM members must commit to. These include:

1.1 Contribute to society and human well-being.
1.2 Avoid harm to others.
1.3 Be honest and trustworthy.
1.4 Be fair and take action not to discriminate.
1.5 Honor property rights including copyrights and patent.

1.6 Give proper credit for intellectual property.
1.7 Respect the privacy of others.
1.8 Honor confidentiality.

In Principle 1.4, the document expands on the issue of fairness:

> *Inequities between different groups of people may result from the use or misuse of information and technology. In a fair society, all individuals would have equal opportunity to participate in, or benefit from, the use of computer resources regardless of race, sex, religion, age, disability, national origin or other such similar factors.*

The Institute of Electrical and Electronics Engineers Code of Ethics, adopted in 1990, is quite similar. And in his paper on "Service-Learning and Engineering Ethics" (1998), Michael Pritchard concludes

> *Although the National Society of Professional Engineers [NSPE] (1996) and the American Society of Civil Engineers [ASCE] (1996) provisions are rather broadly stated, they do provide a rationale for concluding that, at least from the perspective of two major professional engineering societies, community service is an important feature of engineering ethics. (2)*

The We-Must-Address-the-Requirement-of-Our-Accreditation-Boards Argument: The Computer Science Accreditation Commission has established criteria for computer science programs. Under "Additional Areas of Study" it states that:

> *IV-15. The oral communications skills of the student must be developed and applied in the program.*
> *IV-16. The written communications skills of the student must be developed and applied in the program.*
> *IV-17. There must be sufficient coverage of social and ethical implications of computing to give students an understanding of a broad range of issues in this area.*

The Accreditation Board for Engineering and Technology (ABET) has adopted the following criteria effective for the 1999-2000 accreditation cycle for engineering technology programs. Under section I.C.5.b. (General Criteria; Curriculum Elements; Communications, Humanities, and Social Sciences; Social Sciences/Humanities), one finds this statement:

> *It is important that the student acquire an appreciation and understanding of our rich cultural heritage, the complexities of interpersonal relationships, an understanding of the interrelationship between technology and society, and a system of values essential for intelligent and discerning judgments. (1998)*

It should be noted that this criterion falls under the heading of "Social Sciences/Humanities." Thus, the option remains that teaching about the interrelationship between technology and society could occur in courses outside technology proper.

Objections to Modifying the Curriculum

I would like to believe that these calls to address the social impact of technology would be sufficient to inspire our colleagues to embrace teaching methodologies that address these goals. Unfortunately, many remain unconvinced. The general attitude of technology faculty is well represented by the following remarks made in a letter to the *Communications of ACM* in response to an NSF-funded project calling for the infusion of ethics and issues of social impact into the computer science curriculum:

> *The most glaring problem with the proposed, "Implementing a Tenth Strand in the CS Curriculum" . . . is that the proposed subject matter is not computer science. The content of the "strand" has no algorithms, no data structures, no mathematical analysis, no computer architecture, neither software development nor hardware design, no computer science theory. In short, the content is devoid of every standard element present in computer science research and education. . . .*
>
> *A course in social and ethical impact of computing may be desirable, but let us ask the philosophy, sociology, and public policy departments to teach such courses. Etinterests, and doctoral degrees in ethics, not by computer science professors pretending to be ethicists. . . .*
>
> *Ethical and shics should be taught by faculty with experience, research ocial concerns may be important, but as debating the morality of nuclear weapons is not doing physics, discussing the social and ethical impact of computing is not doing computer science. (quoted in Herkert 1998: 20)*

If this does indeed represent the general attitude of the technology professoriate, then arguments for civic education within these disciplines may well fall on deaf ears. Not surprisingly, in nearly 70 percent of the ABET-accredited institutions in one study, there was no ethics-related course requirement for all students (Stephan 1998). When the results of this study are normalized to account for the number of graduates per institution, nearly 80 percent of engineering graduates attend schools with no such ethics-related course requirement. My own informal survey of local universities (California State Universities, the University of California, and private schools) elicited comments such as these:

Off the record, we don't do much with social impact or ethics here.

Our 168 course is already stretched too thin in its current format. I'm a big fan of community-based research, but even at our land-grant college, it seems pretty rare.

Accreditation requirements are collegewide rather than at the department level. I am not sure how seriously it is taken, since most is dealt with in a course outside of the department.

As for myself, I think the idea of teaching people to be ethical by making them take a course is highly suspect.

To strengthen the case for the value of community-based education we must demonstrate that the lessons learned speak directly to the learning outcomes of the professional disciplines. These lessons will not be "data structures" and "algorithms," but they do constitute valuable and significant preparation for a technology professional.

Experiential Learning

Engineering and information technology faculty are no strangers to experiential learning. We certainly embrace the notion that one cannot learn the complexities of our disciplines without doing. Our course requirements are replete with extensive laboratory assignments, and we wouldn't consider graduating a student who had not demonstrated significant skill in the design and development of sophisticated projects.

The eminent psychologist Carl Rogers (1969) explained the importance of experiential learning this way:

Let me define a bit more precisely the elements which are involved in such significant or experiential learning. It has a quality of personal involvement — the whole person in both his feeling and cognitive aspects being in the learning event. It is self-initiated. Even when the impetus or stimulus comes from the outside, the sense of discovery, of reaching out, of grasping and comprehending, comes from within. It is pervasive. It makes a difference in the behavior, the attitudes, perhaps even the personality of the learner. It is evaluated by the learner. He knows whether it is meeting his need, whether it leads toward what he wants to know, whether it illuminates the dark area of ignorance he is experiencing. The locus of evaluation, we might say, resides definitely in the learner. Its essence is meaning. When such learning takes place, the element of meaning to the learner is built into the whole experience. (5)

Outside of our coursework proper, we also support experiential learning opportunities in the corporate world. Most programs have a cooperative education or internship component that allows students to earn academic credit for professional experience. That experiential learning opportunities such as these are more readily acceptable than are community-based experiences stems from a sense that the corporate environment is richer in technology, more advanced in the tools of the trade, so that a student immersed in this environment will be enriched from exposure to the latest technical trends. A community-based experience, on the other hand, as complex as it may be in social issues, usually offers an antiquated or dysfunctional technical environment where students are more knowledgeable than those they work with. What can be learned here? I would like to suggest, quite a lot.

Learning Outcomes From Community-Based Learning

A variety of studies have recently appeared on changes in the attitudes of students involved in community service (for example, Myers-Lipton 1996). The majority of these studies have measured students' commitment to working in their communities after a volunteer experience, and their outcomes consistently show that such students develop a greater empathy for others and a greater sense of the importance of community involvement. Fewer studies have been done on the cognitive and intellectual development of service-learning students, but a recent book by Janet Eyler and Dwight Giles (1999) explores the question of academic learning in a new way.

Studies documenting service-learning outcomes show that students who perform service report that they "learn more" but that measures based on grade-point average and course grades show inconsistent results. However, Eyler and Giles argue that these measures are too narrow and that there are dimensions to academic learning not available to traditional students that service-learning addresses. In particular, they note that the service students they studied had become "more thoughtful and effective," that they "had obtained a deeper, more complex understanding of issues and felt more confident about using what they had learned." The authors argue that such a more complex understanding is a key outcome of the service-learning experience, and they set about to study it in detail. The instrument they developed to do so, a preservice and postservice directed interview, can be found in their text. In the end they conclude that

> *Students in classes where service and learning are well integrated through classroom focus and reflection are more likely to demonstrate greater issue*

knowledge, have a more realistic and detailed personal political strategy, and give more complex analysis of causes of and solutions to the problem. (81)

It should be noted that these positive results apply to courses where the service-learning is done right, i.e., is "well integrated." When this is the case, students demonstrate a greater understanding of the complexity of real-world problems. As technology educators, we must ask: "Is such an outcome important to the preparation of *our* students?"

Professional Preparation From Service Experiences

In this final section I will turn directly to the question of the significance of the learning acquired through service. I will do this in a personal way — by reflecting on the things I have learned from my own community involvement. I have chosen three examples of information and computing system design projects in which I have participated over the last few years: a domestic violence tracking system, a shelter availability for the homeless system, and a computer learning center for a public housing complex.

For very different reasons, the first two projects were never completed. Nonetheless, they point to some of the many lessons to be learned through the design of community-based systems — lessons concerning privacy and security, concerning the importance and impact of technology on individuals, and finally concerning the complexities of real-world problems. I include these case histories for three reasons. First, I hope they will serve to illustrate essential lessons that students need to learn about technology and community. Second, I want to convey the notion that these lessons cannot be adequately addressed in the classroom. And third, I want to suggest that these lessons will not necessarily be addressed in coursework outside our disciplines.

Domestic Violence Information System: I begin with a grant proposal developed with the City of San Francisco Police Department. In 1996, the U.S. Department of Justice issued a request for proposals from local police and judicial departments to apply for funds to improve the response and arrest rate in domestic violence (DV) cases. Colleagues at San Francisco State University had been involved in an earlier successful proposal to obtain laptops for police cruisers in the city, and so we were invited to join the grant-writing team composed of police officials, judges from the local civil and criminal courts, representatives of the district attorney's domestic violence unit, jailers from the Sheriff's Department, and representatives of a network of social service agencies focused primarily on supporting the victims of domestic violence and their families. The team was excellent. The level of cooperation amongst the members was tangible — all were deeply concerned and eager to address the problem areas.

As one can imagine, domestic violence situations in a large metropolitan area such as San Francisco are frequent, dangerous, and highly complex. The diversity of the city's population, for example, required that different approaches be taken with groups accustomed to their own cultural norms. Domestic violence amongst homosexual couples was not uncommon and added an additional dimension to civic response. Compounding the difficulties of the situation was an antiquated information system that had serious shortcomings in design, equipment, training, and use. Here is where I came in — as a consultant on the proposal for a new information system to be funded by the grant.

Accompanied by computer science students, I spent considerable time interviewing the many units of the criminal justice team involved in domestic violence response. The system is elaborate and crosses both jurisdictional and information system boundaries. The complexity of the system, not in the technological sense but in the human sense, was something I have never seen approximated in a classroom lesson.

Frequently, a DV incident begins with a 911 call. The call may be instigated by the victim, the victim's family, or a neighbor who overhears an altercation. The 911 call takers work as a pool adjacent to the pool of computer-aided dispatchers (CADs). The call taker makes a critical first judgment on the severity of the incident. She or he assigns a radio code designating the type of incident and assigns a priority status depending on an impression of the need for immediate response. Once this assignment is made, the call is sent to dispatch. However, call takers do not always tag cases as "DV," and unless they do so, this information is not automatically recorded in the system where it can find a match with relevant court records.

CADs work from a computer screen divided into four sections that provide the list of currently available patrol cars in the field, the prioritized list of active 911 calls, the details of the current call being addressed by the dispatcher, and an area where the dispatcher can query the criminal justice information system (called CABLE). However, because the dispatchers are not sworn officers of the court, they are not authorized to perform searches of the system unless requested to do so.

The potential for danger at the scene dictates that the officers in the field must make the critical judgment of what information they require to deal with the situation at hand. Although the CABLE system provides "query by location" functionality, the officers may not know that a prior call was made from the same location the day before. They may also not know that a "stay away" or "temporary restraining order" (TRO) has been issued for the offender. The officer at the site may choose the typical approach of taking the offender for a walk around the block to cool off. The victim, who has often received a threat of bodily harm (or death) if she or he speaks to the officer, will frequently remain silent. The fact that the officer in the field has not received the information concerning an existing TRO may result in a critical and tragic error.

This is not the only gap in the system. Victims of spousal abuse may go on their own initiative to a civil court to request a TRO. But the civil court record system does not automatically share information with the criminal justice information system, and so this crucial restraint may be lost. In addition, we found that officers who are called to a site on a DV case recorded the information manually, essentially on index cards that were placed in a card file at the station house. Thus, officers on the next shift who are called to the same site might not even know that a response to the same location occurred in the previous 24 hours. And at the jail, the sheriffs might not know that the arrested abuser had been restrained from even calling the spouse. Often, the abuser uses his or her "one call" both to place a threat and to obtain bail money — an occurrence with tragic results.

Meanwhile, back at the courthouse, the assistant district attorney (ADA) works diligently to keep up with an ever-growing and ever-challenging caseload. The ADA we interviewed was completely dedicated to her work, and while we were in her office we witnessed her taking several telephone calls from victims who needed as much emotional as legal support. Naturally, our interests concerned the ADA's link to the information system. She took us down the hall to where the sole terminal available to her entire floor was housed in a closet. Unfortunately, someone had borrowed the user's manual on providing queries to the system; the data transmission speeds were slow; the security codes for access were written on a note posted on the wall; the printer was broken. . . .

In our proposal we identified the following categories of problems in the DV tracking system: Pertinent information was not being collected; information that existed was not being entered into the system; information being entered was not being done so in a timely manner; information available in the system was not accessible to all who needed it; information readily accessible was not being retrieved; retrieved information was not being used properly.

Carl Rogers's (1969) observation concerning "feelings and cognitive aspects being *in* the learning event" was proven throughout the DV project. One's awareness that the information technology system one is designing is critical takes on new meaning as one watches 911 operators handle incoming calls, or witnesses an ADA comforting a victim of abuse, or hears the exasperation in a judge's voice on the ineffectiveness of his court orders, or senses the frustration of the police officers and jailers in dealing with an all-too-frequent crime.

• Watching the dispatchers work at their quad screens was a profound experience in *interface design*. Were the quadrants large enough? Were they placed in the proper position? Should certain functions (such as location checks) be automated? Should the rules of access authorization be reconsidered?

• Talking to the judges and police about the gap in information flow was a profound experience in *system design*. What are the technical issues involved in integrating the criminal justice information system with the civil court system? What are the legal hurdles? What skills do the court officers and district attorney's officers need in order to use the system properly?

• Speaking with officers in the field was a profound experience in *system presentation and performance*. What information is critical? How fast should the information be retrieved? How can performance be enhanced?

In my classes I routinely try to spice up lessons and assignments by referring to actual experiences. However, it is one thing to write in a textbook or laboratory exercise something like "the system you are designing may affect the lives of thousands of individuals" and quite another to speak with those who actually experience it. The former has little more impact than a video game; the latter is all too real. It illuminates for students the complexity of working in the real world and the many layers of issues that must be taken into account when systems are designed.

Public Housing Complex Computer Learning Center: In this second case, I describe a project that is ongoing. Whereas the previous example concerned a project in which advanced students might become involved, this project is more representative of the kind of community service one might provide for beginning students.

Several years ago the university's urban research center, the San Francisco Urban Institute, began working together with the San Francisco Public Housing Authority on plans for the full renovation of one of the housing complexes in the city, Hayes Valley. Hayes had been designated a Campus of Learners by HUD, meaning that funding was available to create a comprehensive learning environment that would address the needs of youth and adult residents alike. The Resident Management Council, an energetic and committed group of residents, had the foresight to request that the common area of the new complex contain a computer learning center and that each of the 108 apartment units in the complex be wired directly to the center. The San Francisco Unified School District donated hundreds of used 486 computers to be installed at Hayes and other housing sites.

The university-community electronic communication project, SFSUnet, has become the host for Hayes Valley Internet activities. SFSUnet had been founded several years prior by university faculty to support the communication needs of local community-based organizations. SFSUnet provides dial-up access to nonprofit agencies, along with email accounts, websites, online database support, asynchronous and real-time conferencing, and more. SFSUnet is entirely staffed with computer science students as system administrators, website developers, database developers, communication facilitators, and the like. Over the years we have supported communication tools for local community-based organizations, statewide art groups such as the California Association of Local Art Agencies, the National Institute for Art and the Disabled, and, most proudly, we hosted the first U.N.-sponsored international online conference on earthquake preparedness.

SFSUnet has proven to be a wonderful vehicle for supporting the service-learning activities of the Computer Science Department. Donations from SUN Microsystems, Oracle, and Cisco have provided the necessary hardware and software. The CS Department offers a course, CSc 695, Computing in the Community, which enlists its students in support of community communication needs through SFSUnet. One semester, for example, CSc 695 students built an elaborate website for a neighborhood organization that contained information on news, recreation, jobs, police reports, and a variety of other topic areas of neighborhood interest.

For the fall 1999 semester, service-learning students had been recruited to inventory, test, and upgrade the computers that have been donated to Hayes. Over a period of four weeks student teams had gone to the Housing Authority warehouse to unpack the computers, determine what operating system and software had been installed, what equipment was working, and what was hopelessly gone. Working side by side with the students were residents of Hayes, some of whom were knowledgeable about computers, and others of whom needed some initial training to be effective.

One of the immediate problems that the students encountered had to do with the lack of software licenses on the applications that came with the donated equipment. Though the systems were configured similarly — same processors, buses, memory, and peripherals — they varied greatly in the software that had been installed. The question came up as to whether we should copy the software from system to system to create a homogeneous set. Certainly it would be desirable to start each unit off with a baseline set of application software. But the students had just finished the section on copyrights in our computing ethics text (Kallman and Grillo 1996), and I did not want to solve this dilemma for the students. It was eventually resolved by the computing center director, a Housing Authority employee, who said that she had received a sizable donation of software from representatives of Microsoft, and was sure that she could go back to them to obtain copies of whatever we needed.

At one meeting I struck up a conversation with a resident about his recent visit to a HUD-organized conference. His story was enlightening. HUD had put out a call for a resident initiative coordinator to be identified for each site, and he had eagerly volunteered hoping to be in a position where he could turn his and others' ideas into new activities at their site. After sitting through three hours of a national HUD meeting where he did not get a chance to speak, he came to the realization that the coordinator position was not being created to coordinate *resident* initiatives, it was being created to coordinate *HUD* initiatives that were to be imposed on the residents. After another three hours, he realized that HUD basically did not believe that residents could take any initiative on their own!

Having worked on this project, the students and I can attest to a vastly different impression. The Hayes Valley Resident Management Council provided the initiative, creativity, and hard work needed to make the renovation plans a reality. The experience changed our attitudes toward the capability of housing residents. It is a lesson that I doubt we could ever have learned in the classroom.

Conclusion

Are these significant lessons for technology students? In the sense that any one would benefit from a better understanding of and respect for one's community, low income or otherwise, certainly. But there were technical lessons, too. For example, as the Hayes Valley computing project continues, students are developing online resources specific to this community. The residents will determine what they want in services — computer-based curricula to obtain the minimal job skills needed to enter the workforce, resources on job opportunities, health and child-care services, start-up businesses, community discussions, and so on. Later on, students will be working as system administrators, trainers, and online software development and support specialists to help make the project successful. They will be working on the development of software tools that directly address community needs. Indeed, we are already experimenting with the ArsDigita Community System developed by Philip Greenspun (1996) at MIT for building online communities. Students are porting, installing, maintaining, and modifying these tools. They are involved in designing, coding, and testing software in a complex environment where the tools are not the latest and the clients are not the most informed. They are honing their technical skills while addressing a critical community need. And perhaps most significantly, they are gaining a full experience of the barriers between technology and those just learning to use it. As they move into professional careers where their jobs will entail bringing this technology to an ever-expanding market, they will be well served by these valuable lessons.

References

Accreditation Board for Engineering and Technology. (1998). *Engineering Criteria 2000.* Available at the ABET website at <http://www.abet.org>.

Eyler, J., and D. Giles. (1999). *Where's the Learning in Service-Learning?* San Francisco, CA: Jossey-Bass.

Greenspun, Philip. (1996). "Philip and Alex's Guide to Web Publishing." <http://photo.net/wtr/thebook/>

Herkert, Joseph R. (1998). "ABET's *Engineering Criteria 2000* and Engineering Ethics: Where Do We Go From Here?" <http://www.onlineethics.org/text/conf/herkert.html>

Kallman, Ernest A., and Grillo, John P. (1996). *Ethical Decision Making and Information Technology: An Introduction With Cases.* New York, NY: McGraw-Hill.

Myers-Lipton, S.J. (1996). "The Effects of Service-Learning on College Students' Levels of Racism." *Michigan Journal of Community Service-Learning* 3: 44-54.

National Telecommunications and Information Administration. (1997). "Falling Through the Net II: New Data on the Digital Divide." <http://www.ntia.doc.gov/ntiahome/net2/falling.html>

Pritchard, Michael. (1998). "Service-Learning and Engineering Ethics." <http://www.onlineethics.org/text/conf/pritchard.html>

Rogers, Carl R. (1969). *Freedom to Learn.* Columbus, OH: Merrill Publishing

Stephan, K.D. (1998). "The Invisible Topic: A Survey of Ethics-Related Instruction in U.S. Engineering Programs." Unpublished manuscript.

Wiener, Norbert. (1954). *The Human Use of Human Beings: Cybernetics and Society.* Boston, MA: Houghton Mifflin.

Service-Learning as a Pedagogy for Engineering: Concerns and Challenges

by Edmund Tsang

The idea of combining service with engineering design projects is not new. In many mechanical or electrical engineering programs, senior capstone design projects are based on providing assistive technology to meet the needs of people with disabilities. However, these capstone design courses are not service-learning courses (nor do the engineering faculty who teach them regard them as such) for at least one important reason: Reflection, which is an essential component of service-learning (Jacoby 1996), plays no formal part in the students' learning strategy. Furthermore, the service provided to the community represents but a single episode in the students' overall college experience. The multilevel learning potential of service has not been integrated into the general course of studies. As a result, whatever social benefit occurs can seem like an afterthought.

Given the thrust of recommendations contained in many recent reports on engineering education reform, it should be obvious by now that "design-across-the-curriculum" can be an effective strategy to achieve the curricular objectives described in those reports (ASEE 1994; NSF 1996). However, as the essays contained in this volume serve to demonstrate, it should also be obvious that service-learning can provide a meaningful context in which to teach engineering design at all stages of a student's academic development. Coupling service-learning with design-across-the-curriculum thus offers an innovative pedagogy to achieve the desirable student outcomes described by the Accreditation Board for Engineering and Technology (ABET 1998) in its publication *Engineering Criteria 2000*.

This chapter will introduce the issue of reflection in engineering. It will also discuss briefly several other challenges and concerns relating to service-learning across the engineering curriculum.

Reflection

Reflection is that component of service-learning that distinguishes it from traditional design projects. It is also that aspect of service-learning that offers the greatest challenge to engineering faculty. Jacoby (1996) defines the goal of student participation in reflection as *[promoting] learning about the larger social issues behind the needs to which their service is responding. This learning includes a deeper understanding of the historical, sociological, cultural, economic, and political contexts of the needs or issues being addressed.* (7)

This goal corresponds quite well with the student performance outcomes described in ABET's *Engineering Criteria 2000*; namely, "knowledge of contemporary issues" and "the broad education necessary to understand the impact of engineering solutions in a global and societal context" (ABET 1998). The challenge is to find models and examples of reflection that are appropriate for the engineering curriculum.

Even though service-learning is much more developed in the humanities and the social sciences, the methods used there to conduct reflection offer little help as models for engineering, because they often ask students to express feelings and emotions as the focus of the reflection process. A cursory review of Jacoby's introduction to service-learning (1996) — yielded the following entries linking reflection with feelings and emotions:

- *Mark D. McCarthy states that it is important in "Postservice Reflection" to bring participants together to "share emotions." McCarthy cites one example in which students talk about "the possible emotions they may feel during and after their service experience," and another example in which students "explore their own thoughts and feelings."* (121)

- *Cesie Delve Scheuermann describes one model of reflection in which the student is asked, "How do I feel about what I see and hear? Why do I feel this way?"* (141)

- *Suzanne D. Mintz and Garry W. Hesser state that "reflection should happen immediately after the [service-learning] experience to discuss . . . feelings."* (31)

- *Keith Morton advocates the use of journals for reflection because "a journal is a safe arena in which students can examine the emotions . . . that may arise from service."* (286)

- *Gail Albert cites an example of reflection in National Service programs in which the journal kept by students "helps them express feelings."* (191)

Many of the methods used to structure reflection in the humanities/social sciences disciplines find little resonance with engineering faculty and students, because of their temperament and their preference for logical, analytical, quantitative, and fact-based methods of inquiry. One possible solution to developing appropriate reflection materials for service-learning in engineering could lie in collaborations between engineering faculty and their colleagues in the humanities and social sciences — either to identify existing course sequences that examine the historical, sociological, cultural, economic, and political contexts of the interaction between technology and society, or to develop new, interdisciplinary courses that support student learning about the larger social issues behind projects requiring engineering expertise. In this way, the course materials developed would address a specific curricular need outlined in *Engineering Criteria 2000*, i.e., that of providing "the broad education necessary to understand the impact of engineering solutions in a global and societal context" (ABET 1998).

A good model for cross-disciplinary scholarship on reflection in service-learning is the NSF-sponsored Workshop to Develop Numerical Problems to Teach Engineering Ethics hosted by Texas A&M University in August 1995. At that five-day workshop, 40 engineering professors gathered by discipline (represented were chemical, civil, electrical and computer, and mechanical engineering) to (1) identify, research, and compose numerical problems and (2) to work out their solutions. Then, with the help of two philosophy/ethics professors, the engineering professors developed the ethical questions that the numerical problems posed for engineers.

Concerns and Challenges

Concerns: The idea of engineering students providing "professional services" through their service-learning projects raises several issues. These include: How professional a service do such projects provide? Are students even capable of rendering professional services? Could service-learning displace the paid services of professional engineers? What about liability?

Clearly, some of these concerns can be more easily addressed than others. For example, service-learning projects cannot replace professional engineering services, for the simple reason that the latter can be provided only by registered engineers. For community organizations and local/state agencies, which often do not have sufficient resources or much technical expertise, what service-learning projects can provide is valuable information that can help those organizations/agencies better understand their needs and whether they should, in fact, seek additional professional services. Relatedly, student efforts in service-learning can be used by community organizations and local/state agencies to leverage outside funding to pay for professional engineering services. Such was the case with the Decker Lake Wetland Preservation Foundation (DLWPF) in Salt Lake County, Utah, the community partner for CE 451, Hydrology, at the University of Utah. DLWPF was able to leverage the work done by engineering students through their service-learning projects as a match to obtain outside funding.

As for liability, there are usually few chances of incurring it through service-learning projects concerned with meeting classroom instructional needs, and where the instructor exercises reasonable prudence and care. In those instances where some chance of incurring liability nevertheless does exist, such as in projects dealing with rehabilitation, physical infrastructure, or the environment, the instructor should consult the institution's policy regarding industry-sponsored projects, particularly senior capstone design projects. Guidelines might already be available, at the college or the university level, to address the liability issues that might arise from service-based projects.

Challenges: Engineering faculty should be aware that scheduling conflicts will always be a challenge in service-learning, because students and their community partners often follow conflicting schedules. Hence, it is important to remind students, at the very beginning of a service-learning project, of the importance of scheduling, and ask them to demonstrate creativity and be persistent in contacting their community partners and in arranging appointments.

Finally, faculty need to be aware that there are some students who do not believe in community service and might even challenge a service-learning assignment.[1] I will refer to one such case in another chapter in this volume.

Note

1. There are a number of essays listed on the Ayn Rand Institute website <http://www.aynrand.org/medialink/> that attack the morality of community service, stating: "It is the opposing morality, 'that of selfishness,' that enables man to achieve his own happiness." One example is "Public Service and Private Misery" by David Harriman, which was published as an editorial in *USA Today* on April 23, 1997.

References

Accreditation Board for Engineering and Technology. (1998). *Engineering Criteria 2000*. Available at the ABET website at <http://www.abet.org>.

American Society for Engineering Education. (1994). *Engineering Education for a Changing World*. A joint project report of the Engineering Deans Council and the Corporate Roundtable of the ASEE. Available at the ASEE website at <http://www.asee.org>.

Jacoby, B. (1996). "Service-Learning in Today's Higher Education." In *Service-Learning in Higher Education: Concepts and Practices*, edited by B. Jacoby and Associates, pp. 3-25. San Francisco, CA: Jossey-Bass.

National Science Foundation. (1996). "Shaping the Future: New Expectations for Undergraduate Education in Science, Mathematics, Engineering, and Technology." NSF report 96-139. Available from the NSF website at <http://www.nsf.gov>.

Service-Learning Reflection for Engineering: A Faculty Guide

by Jennifer Moffat and Rand Decker

Service-learning has caught on and is sweeping through the curricula of academic departments across the country. For many disciplines — psychology, sociology, communication, nursing — incorporating service-learning into a course is a natural extension of the teaching strategies and thinking styles that have been used in those disciplines for decades. Hence, many social science instructors find that conducting the reflection component of service-learning is similar to facilitating other class discussions.

For engineering faculty, however, reflection can present a challenge. There is no silence quite so pregnant as the one when engineers, both faculty and students alike, are asked to talk about how they feel. This is not altogether unexpected. Engineers and physical scientists are trained to take the self out of the problem-solving process. Scientific analysis is the backbone of engineering, and this analysis must occur within a context of objectivity. One's feelings are not supposed to factor into the equation. Hence, this disciplinary culture, coupled with an overwhelming lack of reflective facilitation experience on the part of most engineering faculty, puts the reflection component of service-learning at grave risk in the engineering classroom.

And yet, a number of recent studies, as well as emerging modern accreditation criteria, point to the fact that this general lack of reflection and personal/societal context in engineering education needs to be remedied. The present chapter on service-learning reflection in engineering was prepared as a learning tool and resource for faculty who might be struggling with implementing reflection successfully in their service-learning courses.

The very fact that engineering relies heavily on linear, black-and-white thinking with little room for personal introspection and reflection means that engineering students and faculty alike have a lot to gain from service-learning reflection. Service-learning demands that students consider the gray areas that inevitably arise when dealing with social issues and incorporate them into the problem-solving process. Engineering faculty who implement service-learning in their courses have an opportunity to inspire students to think in new ways that can tap their creativity and make them better engineers and better citizens. The most effective way to tap this creativity is to engage students actively in reflection.

Successful reflection sessions in the classroom help students become familiar with different perspectives and prepare them to appreciate and explore the societal *impact* of engineering. Reflection provides a vital forum for students to discuss creatively their service-learning experiences and to learn from one another. It is, in short, integral to the service-learning process. Indeed, service without adequate reflection can actually reinforce negative stereotypes and unquestioning adherence to oversimplified solutions. For instance, students helping a small community organization with a hydrology project were frustrated with the citizens' lack of response to the project at a community meeting. During class reflection the students came to realize that they themselves did not get involved in their own communities to the degree they should. Thus, they began to reassess their roles as engaged citizens. Thanks to a purposeful discussion about what had happened, the students' frustration became a valuable learning experience.

Presented in the following pages are ideas on how to communicate the importance of reflection in service-learning to engineering students, as well as specific teaching strategies to make service-learning more meaningful, applicable, and exciting.

Reflection: What Is It and How Does It Work?

> *Experience is not what happens to you. It is what you do with what happens to you.*
>
> — Aldous Huxley

> *Reflection is simply another word for learning. What distinguishes it from some other forms of learning is that "reflection" grows out of experience.*
>
> — Keith Morton, associate director,
> Feinstein Center for Public Service,
> Providence College

As noted here and in other chapters in this volume, a significant portion of the learning in service-learning takes place when students spend time thinking about and discussing their service experience and how it relates to their coursework. Reflection is the time one provides for oneself and for students to think critically about issues raised by working in the community and how scientific and engineering concepts and skills relate to those issues. By facilitating reflection, the engineering instructor provides students with an opportunity to learn from their experiences and from others' experiences and perceptions.

For someone to become an effective reflection leader, he or she must be familiar with the way reflection works. Reflection is not such an unfamiliar concept. Anytime one reads a book or an article or has a conversation to expand the context of and find meaning in one's work, one is experiencing something similar to reflection. Reflection allows one to draw connections between what one discusses in the classroom and what one experiences in the real world. Becoming aware of one's reflection experiences and recognizing the reflection techniques already present in one's routine provide a wealth of experiences to draw on when engaging students in service-learning reflection.

Perhaps the single most useful step one can take in becoming a successful reflection facilitator in engineering is attending service-learning faculty meetings on campus. Such meetings are typically gatherings of faculty from across the disciplines, faculty with diverse backgrounds and perspectives as well as a wealth of information and experience. Indeed, many have themselves grappled with questions similar to those the beginner must address. Thus, the lessons already learned by other faculty can be instrumental in helping solve reflection problems that arise during one's service-learning courses.

Reflection: Questions for Engineers

Reflection most often takes place in the classroom in the form of a discussion. During reflection sessions, an instructor listens closely to all participants. Although the instructor should have an idea of what he or she wants students to learn from their experiences, he or she must also be prepared to adjust the line of questioning to help them expand on the themes they encounter as they think about their experiences. Hence, discussion questions should be open-ended and flexible, but not chosen randomly.

The instructor can create questions from his or her own relevant experience, can draw from articles read, comments students have made in their journals, or suggestions from other faculty. It is good to remember that if an instructor is encountering certain issues through his or her work as an engineer, the students may very well be encountering similar issues. Through service-learning reflection, these issues can be brought to the surface in a way that helps engineering students examine the social and community context of their work. Given below are a few sample questions that are particularly relevant to engineering classes. They are also typical of the generic, probing, open-ended questions that spur successful reflection:

1. *Is there a difference between the way engineers view problems and the way people in other professions view them? What are the differences? Why do these differences exist?*

2. *What nontechnical information did you learn about the project from the people you worked with? Is this information relevant to your work? If so, why?*

3. How can engineers and citizens work together to solve problems? Why should they?

4. Do you have an ethical dilemma about taking on the project? Have you been asked to do something that contradicts your values or beliefs? Are there social issues that affect or are affected by the project you have been assigned; and if so, how will you take them into account? What is the ultimate outcome of your project? Who will benefit?

5. How has the nature of engineering changed since the end of the Cold War? How does this affect your work?

6. If you put this project on a resume, would you list it as "community service"? Does the engineering community value volunteer work? Why or why not?

7. Is there a difference between what we think is needed and what the recipients of the service think is needed? How do you know? [One would hope students have spoken directly with the recipients of the service!] Will this relate to your work in the future? Why is this important?

8. Think of a scientific principle that can be applied to help you understand a social problem. How does your thought process as an engineer affect the way you view social issues? Can social issues affect the way you work as an engineer?

9. What are the stereotypes of engineers? Are they true? If so, in what circumstances is it critical that they be true? In what circumstances are these stereotypes an impediment to successful community service?

10. Is there a role for and mechanism for you to continue providing engineering assistance to the community after graduation? Is this activity important?

Finally, the instructor should make sure the students know that he or she is learning along with them through the discussion-reflection process.

Reflection Tools: Activities

Reflection activities serve many purposes. They can be used to start discussions, encourage creative thinking, and facilitate communication among students. Using different activities during reflection sessions provides a means of communication for students not comfortable with open discussion. Reflection activities can be especially helpful in making a transition from lecture format to discussion format in the classroom. Described below are a few reflection activities and how they can be used to help solve problems that might arise in discussions of student experiences. Many of these activities serve multiple purposes.

Taking Sides

As the instructor reads questions, individual students stand in clusters according to the answers with which they concur. (This activity can be modified if there is limited space or mobility by having students use thumbs-up signals to express their opinions or by having them stand in a line to represent a spectrum of opinions.) Between questions, students in the different clusters are asked to explain why they chose their answers. (In most cases, there will be no strictly right or wrong answers.) Some enjoyable, warm-up questions might include whether campus athletics should be funded with student fees or how students feel about current events. Once participants are comfortable with this format, they can be steered toward questions relating to their service project. The requirement that students physically move about the classroom makes this activity useful when they appear tired or disengaged. Creating a mechanism for everyone to express an opinion encourages students to feel invested and become more involved.

What Is This?

The instructor provides an object or a picture of an object for students to look at. (Ideally that object is somehow related to the class's service-learning project.) The class is first asked what the object is, what it is used for, and why it is important. Then it is asked whether an architect would agree, or a lumberjack, or a teacher, or a child. Do different perspectives on an object affect the way people see and react? This line of questioning can eventually lead to a discussion of stereotypes and perspectives among different groups in society and why it is important to learn to work with different perspectives. The activity is especially useful when students are having difficulty accepting the various perspectives being expressed by classmates, the instructor, and community service agencies and recipients.

Wall Exercises

The instructor begins by posting newspaper clippings, stories, quotes, etc., around the room, along with blank sheets of paper on which students can write their reactions. (The materials should pertain in some way to the topic under discussion.) Then the students are asked to walk silently around the room, reading each panel and writing their opinions on the paper provided. When they have finished, selected students are asked to read the written opinions out loud as a prelude to group discussion. This activity can be used when students are too shy to express opinions in a standard discussion format, or when an instructor has material to share with students in a creative way.

Concentric Circles

Students are asked to form two equal circles, one inside the other. The inner circle turns to face the outer circle so that everyone is facing a partner. Then a question or unfinished statement is read to the class. Partners introduce themselves, and each takes a minute to respond to the question or complete the statement and explain his or her opinion. After all the students have had a chance to respond, one circle is rotated so everyone gets a new partner. The process continues for several rounds before the questioning is turned into a general discussion. This activity is useful for helping students become comfortable with expressing their opinions to one person so they will feel less intimidated with the whole class.

Notecards

Students form groups of four or five, preferably with people they don't know. Each group is given a notecard with a quotation or question that deals with engineering and service-learning, and each student is asked to respond within his or her group. The individual groups then explain to the rest of the class what they have discussed. This is a creative way to start general class discussions and builds students' skills in formulating a consensus of opinions.

Case Studies

An instructor uses case studies that outline dilemmas similar to those students might experience while working on their service-learning projects. One way to use cases is to reduce them to a few sentences, write them on cards, and hand the cards out to groups of four or five students. The groups are given 20-30 minutes to discuss solutions. Then they report their solutions to the class as a whole. Students can also be asked to come up with their own cases, perhaps based on personal experience. This is a good way to help clarify expectations before a project begins.

Nonverbal In-Class Responses

In-class discussion-reflection need not take place orally. Students can also be asked to respond to reflection questions in writing. Relevant questions can be read aloud, written on the board, or prepared as worksheets. This kind of activity is useful in allowing introverted students to reflect and in helping students organize their thoughts before or after a class discussion.

Reflection Tools: Journals

Journals are a vital part of the reflection process. The time students spend thinking and writing about their experiences complements the time spent in class discussion sessions. Some students who find it difficult to write about their experiences in nontechnical terms may find discussion sessions much easier and more productive, but journals provide an important way to evaluate the students who do not speak up in class. However, probably the single most important benefit of journals is that they prompt students to notice what they are experiencing and to evaluate their service experience through introspection. Hence, journals are especially valuable in that they can be used to help engineering students shift over from an objective to a more subjective mode of analysis.

There are many ways to approach journal assignments. Regardless of the specific approach, an instructor must always begin by making his or her expectations clear. Students need to understand how journal entries differ from entries in an engineering log or field book. Journal assignments should encourage students to express opinions, describe reactions to service experiences, and consider questions that arise in the course of the project. To be sure, reflection journal activities can be coupled with an engineering log. In this way, students can learn by juxtaposing their traditional engineering notes with service-learning reflection. In any event, it is important that students receive specific journaling guidelines.

Some instructors may find it difficult to give students enough freedom to encourage self-expression while providing sufficient structure to assess and grade their performance. Providing specific questions for students to respond to will help them focus and help the instructor gauge how much effort they are investing in the assignment. Furthermore, grades should be based not on the opinions expressed but on students' willingness to think seriously about their experience. Still another way to give them direction in making their entries is to provide a format. An instructor can, for example, ask them to outline the *facts* of their experience separately from their *thoughts and opinions* regarding that experience.

Should it be necessary, a journal activity called "perspective writing" can be used to help students begin to think more subjectively. In this activity, they write from the perspective of one of the recipients of the service. They might describe the project and its goals from this perspective, then compare how and why this perspective differs from their own. Perspective writing can help reinforce empathy and can help students understand how the service recipients view them as service providers.

Finally, an instructor should consider double-entry journaling. In this approach, students divide their paper into two sides lengthwise. They then use this divided paper to separate facts from opinions and thoughts. Some examples include:

Left Side	Right Side
Describe a typical project visit.	Why do you think X happened?
Describe some of your interactions.	What role did you play in these activities?
What is the most difficult part of your work?	What do you feel like when you are onsite?
Describe the equipment that you use.	Would you work at this place for a living? Why or why not?
What is the service you are providing?	How do you feel about the people you serve?
Describe the people you met today.	How do they regard you?

The time students spend writing reflectively in journals will help ensure a much more rewarding service-learning experience. As they write, and as they look back on their writing, they will come to recognize the subtle shifts in perspective they have experienced during the course of their work.

Conclusion

As engineering, technology, and society become more intertwined and interdependent, service-learning can provide an ever more effective way for instructors to help students acquire the skills and perspectives that will allow students to use their technical knowledge to improve the community and make their careers more meaningful and fulfilling. Providing opportunities for reflection can be challenging for faculty, but investing time and creativity in mastering this pedagogical skill can be rewarding and exciting for all involved. There are few, if any, irreparable errors one can make in learning to facilitate reflection in engineering classes, except perhaps not trying at all.

Suggested Readings

Accreditation Board for Engineering and Technology. (1998). *Engineering Criteria 2000.* Available at the ABET website at <http://www.abet.org>.

American Society for Engineering Education. (1994). *Engineering Education for a Changing World.* A joint project report of the Engineering Deans Council and the Corporate Roundtable of the ASEE. Available on the ASEE website at <http://www.asee.org>.

Astin, A.W. (1996). "The Role of Service-Learning in Higher Education." *About Campus* 1(1): 15-19.

——— . (October 1995). "What Higher Education Can Do in the Cause of Citizenship." *The Chronicle of Higher Education*, B1-B2.

Boyer, E.L. (March 9, 1994). "Creating the New American College." *The Chronicle of Higher Education*, A48.

Cisneros, H.G. (February 1995). "The University and the Urban Challenge." Washington, DC: U.S. Department of Housing and Urban Development.

de Acosta, M. (Fall 1995). "Journal Writing in Service-Learning: Lessons From a Mentoring Project." *Michigan Journal of Community Service-Learning* 2: 141–149.

National Science Foundation. (1996). "Shaping the Future: New Expectations for Undergraduate Education in Science, Mathematics, Engineering, and Technology." NSF report 96-139. Available from the NSF website at <http://www.nsf.gov>.

Miller, Stephen. (1996). "Science and Society: Redefining the Relationship." Providence, RI: Campus Compact.

National Society for Experiential Education. (1995). *Combining Service and Learning: Resource Guide*. Raleigh, NC: National Society for Experiential Education.

Parsons, Cynthia. (1996). *Serving to Learn, Learning to Serve: Civics and Service From A to Z*. Thousand Oaks, CA: Corwin Press.

How to Institutionalize Service-Learning Into the Curriculum of an Engineering Department: Designing a Workable Plan

by Peter T. Martin and James Coles

Our universities have been characterized as "ivory towers" where a privileged intellectual elite pursues narrow research interests. Some question the relevance of our academic courses and our commitment to teaching. We are accused of detachment from our local communities. One of the ways in which the University of Utah is tackling these negative associations is through service-learning. A class can be designated "service-learning" if it addresses a community problem through the practical application of theory provided formally in class. In this way, students learn to understand how theoretical principles enable professionals to help communities solve their problems.

Service-learning can be described as experiential learning through the integration of traditional classroom teaching with structured community service. It represents the application of academic knowledge to the genuine needs of the community and its organizations. Service-learning is more than an internship, more than volunteering. It is a managed merging of theory and practice that requires students to reflect on and assess the value of their applied academic experience. Engineering curricula invariably offer projects. Students have to apply design principles to real or contrived problems. Service-learning, as practiced in civil and environmental engineering at the University of Utah, is more challenging. Not only do our students design within a project framework, but they also address a real problem. They have to listen to the community, speak back through their designs, and then reflect on the value of the process.

Engineering professionals must occupy two distinct realms. First, they must develop, manipulate, and deduce engineering science. Second, they must interpret and explain their techniques to the public they serve. One of the more difficult things to teach engineering students is how engineers communicate their technical expertise to the community. It is through service-learning that engineering students can come to appreciate the relevance of their study and develop essential communication skills. The bringing together of a university course and a community need creates new learning opportunities.

Service-learning did not begin with engineering faculty. The pioneers were social scientists and academics in the arts and humanities. That engineers often insist on a fee for their services could be seen as a negation of the entire concept of community service so central to service-learning. Indeed, many engineering faculty fail to understand the unique educational opportunities offered by service-learning. Some even feel that the relationship between the engineer and the community is irrelevant to an engineering education.

In the Department of Civil and Environmental Engineering at the University of Utah, service-learning offers the opportunity to draw the relevance of liberal learning into the engineering curriculum. When engineering majors are encouraged to apply liberal learning concepts to classes with technical service projects, the possibility of synergy across the curriculum arises. Furthermore, in addition to supporting engineering education in a more technical sense, service-learning contributes to preparing engineering students for citizenship. By showing them the relevance of their learning to the community, service-learning enhances their civic awareness.

Civil Engineering Design

Civil engineers are trained in design — itself a complex process. Teaching students design has been tackled in a variety of ways. At the University of Utah, service-learning provides one design track. But before discussing the actual role of service-learning, we should first explain the eight-step iterative procedure that constitutes the design process in civil engineering. Here, the design of a bridge serves as the illustrative example:

Step 1. Define the problem: location (where), span (size), load (how strong), demand (how many users). Large quantities of information have to be collected.

Step 2. Identify variable factors: structural (what kind of bridge), transportation (road, rail, combination), geotechnical (good ground, poor ground). For each variable identified, a set of cost estimates is drafted.

Step 3. Set evaluation criteria: what are the measures that will distinguish each alternative? These may include appearance (how prominent), cost (what is the budget), design (1-in-100-year flood, earthquake-resistant), construction (can it be built quickly, and is that important), maintenance budget (steel needs paint, other materials weather gracefully).

Step 4. Generate multiple solutions: this is a creative stage whereby as many alternatives as possible are identified regardless of cost or effectiveness.

Step 5. Evaluate alternatives: according to the criteria established in Step 3. Alternatives will be graded to provide a quantitative assessment and will be ranked according to a subjective or qualitative measure.

Step 6. Select alternative and recommend: the client (city, state, federal) is presented with a reasoned case for the preferred alternative. All technical information is provided but interpreted for "lay consumption." It is here that the work is documented. The ideas are communicated through presentations, drawings, text, and cost estimates.

Step 7. Client selects design alternative: often, this is a lengthy process involving many constituents including local communities.

Step 8. Return to Step 1 with narrowed constraints: continue through subsequent steps, etc. With many parameters defined and fewer alternatives, the civil engineer returns to the problem-definition stage with more focus. In the case of a small project, these steps could be completed in one pass. For a large infrastructure project, they could run through many iterations, taking years or even decades.

Civil engineering design is not normally taught within a service-learning context. Its traditional teaching philosophy can be described as subject-based learning. Students are told about what they need to know. Next they learn what they need to know. Finally, they work on problems that require them to apply their new-found knowledge. Subject-based learning is usually associated with a structured textbook; each section beginning with theory, followed by concrete examples, and finally problems. In design, this traditional approach, of necessity, has to begin with a problem already identified. It is difficult to incorporate evaluation and client components without resorting to a project approach.

Problem-based learning is very different. The process begins with the posing of a problem. This may be presented or the students themselves may formulate their problem. Thus, the first stage is exploratory, creating hypotheses and identifying issues. The next stage is often clumsy. Here students attempt to solve the problem using their existing knowledge. With careful guidance, the instructor enables them to identify existing relevant knowledge, which will lead to clarification of the new knowledge necessary for solving the problem. Students are then guided in acquiring the new knowledge and are helped, perhaps in a formal way. Individual study or group study can be applied at this stage. Next, it is important that the new ideas be shared. Here, the instructor plays a pivotal role in ensuring that all new ideas are shared among students. Equipped with the new knowledge, students tackle the problems they faced before. For an excellent discussion of the distinction between subject-based and problem-based learning, the reader is referred to ASEE's "Let Problems Drive the Learning in Your Classroom" (1996).

To summarize, subject-based learning begins with theory and ends with an application. Problem-based learning begins with a problem that leads to theory, which is then brought back to the original problem. Service-learning in the Department of Civil and Environmental Engineering at the University of

Utah is problem-based. Students access theory in response to a community concern formulated as an engineering problem.

Since service-learning provides an opportunity to replace subject-based learning with problem-based learning, the Department of Civil and Environmental Engineering has adopted it to help weave a design theme across the curriculum.

Service-Learning Across the Departmental Curriculum

The objective is to create a set of undergraduate and graduate courses from each of the five core civil and environmental engineering disciplines: transportation, structural, geotechnic, water, and environmental engineering. With the plan in place and functioning properly, no students will be able to graduate without at least one service-learning course on their transcript. The plan contains the following four components:

- Criteria for the identification of a service-learning course.
- A supplement to the departmental policy guidelines on tenure and promotion to support and reward faculty sponsoring service projects.
- A mentoring guide for new faculty.
- Guidance on student assessment.

Criteria for Identification of a Service-Learning Course

In establishing a plan to institutionalize service-learning, we must first identify what qualifies as service-learning. In this regard, the Department of Civil and Environmental Engineering is guided by the following descriptive criteria:

- Students provide a needed service to individuals, organizations, or other community entities.
- The service experience relates to the subject matter of the course, and students are required to show that they have related the service to that subject matter.
- The service-learning unit is actively assessed.
- Community partners/participants are informed of the needs of the students and are required to contribute to the evaluation of the quality of the service provided.
- While projects naturally help prepare students for careers, the focus of the service is in the development of civic education.
- Projects are established in such a way that participants can share their learning.

Having clearly identified what service-learning entails, the plan turns to recognition of its value to the department by including service-related activities in the department's tenure and promotion policy.

A Supplement to the Departmental Policy Guidelines on Tenure and Promotion to Support and Reward Faculty Sponsoring Service Projects

Introducing service-learning courses that in many ways break with more traditional teaching strategies means that such a move might be professionally risky. Students can be reluctant to accept new teaching approaches, and faculty, fearful of poor student evaluations, can be disinclined to try service-learning. As one way of encouraging service-learning across the departmental curriculum, promotion and tenure criteria should be adjusted to recognize service-learning as a valid pedagogy. The Department of Civil and Environmental Engineering has taken its cue in this regard from the university's Bennion Center. The department's promotion and tenure guidelines now include the following service-learning criteria:

- The faculty member's service-learning contributions relate to her or his area of scholarship.
- The faculty member's service-learning is responsive to the needs of the community and industry.
- The service-learning in question enables students to understand the true relevance of their studies.
- The service-learning in question has broadened students' professional and civic understanding.

In reviewing a candidate's performance, the tenure and promotion committee draws on the following questions:

- What are the effects of service-learning on the instructor's teaching and research?
- Are there any publications, community projects, or presentations arising out of the service-learning course(s)?
- Do excerpts from student assignments describe how the faculty member's work influenced the community and the learning experience?

A Mentoring Guide for New Faculty

Though the nature of service-learning courses varies, a useful template for the structure of a typical civil engineering service-learning course would be as follows:

Prior to the beginning of the course, a project is selected. Identification of a community need could come about through a government department (municipal or state) or directly from a local community source. The course is set up so that the students decide how to approach the problem. Whom will they receive input from? Where and how will they collect data? What is the time line for completing the project? Students should make presentations of their findings to the public with visual aids and leave sufficient time to answer questions.

Reflection is that aspect of service-learning that enables students to look at their learning experiences. Class time should be set aside for discussion of logistics, sharing information, practice presentations, brainstorming ideas, and overall assessment of how a project is proceeding. Students should keep project journals in which they record their progress and respond to issues raised by community groups.

A well-organized service-learning course has a number of players, and each of them has a role and attendant responsibility. A comprehensive personnel list would include the students, the instructor, a teaching assistant, a community contact, the community group, and a professional contact. For a service-learning course to function effectively, roles must be defined clearly at the very outset of the course. The instructor provides material to assist the students in completing their community project and participates in class reflection discussions. If available, a teaching assistant coordinates the community project to provide continuity throughout the course and makes contacts with community groups and with the professional contact. The professional contact provides background information and context on the community project and helps provide engineering data. The students are responsible for completing and presenting the project. The community group, which is usually formed from a preexisting organization, participates by attending briefings and presentations.

Students evaluate their learning experience through classroom discussions and through service-learning course evaluation forms. This process must clearly differentiate itself from the routine instructor evaluation. Its goal is to reflect, measure, and assess the value of the community service as delivered. Its purpose is to enhance student learning. It is not specifically designed to improve the quality of future courses. By involving the community group, the process addresses the effectiveness of the student contribution, thereby showing students how they might improve their future service to the community.

Having established a typical course profile, the guide can turn to specific suggestions. The following list will grow as more and more faculty register their experiences.

- Service-learning courses demand more advance preparation than do conventional courses. Plan service-learning courses two semesters ahead of time.
- Match the task to the capabilities of the students — freshman students tackle freshman projects.
- While most of the work is "up-front," mentoring during the semester is vital. Service-learning is too new to run like a traditional design project, because there is no culture of service-learning and older students will not have prepared newer students.
- The effort should be front-loaded with early community meetings and

coursework deliverables. This applies to many courses but is especially important with service-learning courses.

- Clarify your expectations of the scope of student design and ensure that community expectations are consistent through early open communication. Even with modest expectations, there are often unpleasant surprises, and from the unlikeliest sources among the students.
- You will need a trained teaching assistant. The university has a pool of experienced TAs and helps with training. When setting up your first course, get trained alongside your TA.
- Seek external support for TAs. When a community group approaches you with a suitable service-learning project, ask the group to contribute to supporting a TA. A thousand dollars buys plenty of valuable TA support.
- Substantial class time should be set aside to discuss the community project. You must treat the project as the centerpiece of your course; otherwise it will not be an educational vehicle. Students need class time to focus their energies.
- If you plan to have your students present their ideas to a community group, have them practice their presentations in class. Be fulsome in your feedback.
- Encourage your students to invest their time with community groups at the outset of the project, thereby reducing the chances of alienation and opposition. Students will learn that even with early and close communication, some people will remain skeptical of their motives.
- Invite neighborhood leaders to class within the first couple of weeks of the course. Encourage your students to listen to the concerns of the neighborhood residents and help them define their criteria for success.
- Attend neighborhood meetings regularly. Keep residents up-to-date on research, conflicts, and difficulties. Remain open to community members' ideas throughout the design process.
- If you can, set up an information survey hot line. Record information about the students' designs. Prepare a menu of options for callers to select. Advertise community meetings through flyers, bulletins, and newspaper features.
- Conduct a thorough door-to-door or mail survey. Organize the survey with options from which respondents can choose, not just open space for comments. This helps focus the evaluation process.
- Include all affected groups in the design process. Invite all interested parties to the initial meeting and maintain open communication with them throughout the semester. Neglecting one community group can spoil the credibility of the final report.
- Arrange a small budget before the beginning of the semester. Making flyers, mailing surveys, advertising a hot line, printing, and renting space for

meetings cost money. The budget should be documented, and funding arrangements should be clarified early on. In some cases, costs might be picked up by the government agency associated with the project.

Guidance on Student Assessment

Student assessment has two parts: the learning achieved by the students and the quality of the service provided. Traditional methods of assessing student learning are not always appropriate for a service-learning course. A quiz or midterm test cannot identify whether a student has grasped how the fundamentals of engineering are applied in a concrete service project. Better devices are reflective journals, class discussions, peer evaluation, term papers, and engineering reports. However, with regard to reports, the departmental plan differs from mainstream engineering expectations in one important way. Given that civil engineers are called on to write reports for their clients, the plan recognizes that service projects must include such a written component. Here, however, the reports target a community group rather than other engineers. In this way, service-learning in civil engineering extends the scope of student writing and presentation skills by shifting their focus from professional communication with peers to professional communication with the community.

There must also be both formal and informal outside assessment of the service project. As many players as possible should be allowed to evaluate the quality of the service provided. Sometimes an evaluation is completed only after the class has concluded and it could come in an unconventional form; e.g., a media response or electronic dialogue. This feedback is nonetheless valuable to the students. For this reason, teachers are encouraged to maintain contact with class members even after the course has concluded.

Plan Implementation Steps

With agreement on the four components just described, implementation of the departmental plan requires a series of eight steps:

1. Develop a clear statement of the criteria that will determine what constitutes a service-learning course, component, or element. This statement must be consistent with the mission statement of the department, which in turn is consistent with the goals of the college and the university.

2. Modify existing courses that already meet some of the criteria required to qualify as service-learning.

3. Develop new classes from preliminary experimental miniprojects.

4. Sponsor a faculty member as a University Public Service Professor. (Such professors receive small grants to support individual service-learning initiatives.)

5. Uphold the principle that once tested in the experimental stage, a service-learning course should be sustained within the curriculum.

6. Encourage collaboration among faculty through interdisciplinary projects and cross-departmental cooperation.

7. Commit the department to support service-learning with travel funds, conference attendance, research assistance, and secretarial support.

8. Document the plan as a written statement.

Discussion

Civil and environmental engineering is defined as the science of wisely using the finite resources of nature for the benefit of mankind while protecting the environment. Civil engineers, like all professional engineers, are subject to liability concerns. We design and build huge infrastructure projects such as freeways, dams, airports, and harbors. We spend vast sums of public money and have the safety of countless people in our hands.

The risk of unsafe designs to the community is daunting. From Roman times on, avoiding risk has led to a conservative bias among civil engineers. The maxim has been: Better to err through overdesign and waste some of that public money than to provide cheaper structures that are risky. Such a sense of responsibility brings a new dimension to the notion of service. Engineers must contract with their communities, somewhat in the way a surgeon will only operate from within the protection of the medical profession.

Hence, civil engineers cannot serve without a formal framework that protects the interests of the community and individual professionals alike. Here is the challenge of introducing service-learning to the next generation of engineers: how to introduce the notion of service when everything we do must be formally contracted with financial considerations.

One outcome of the systematic introduction of service-learning across the curriculum is that students learn how their various skills fit into the matrix of community imperatives and political process. Their designs are challenged by community groups encouraged to be constructively critical. This teaches the students accountability, which is pivotal to the role of a professional engineer. The community gets to voice its concerns to an informed group devoid of political pressure. Vague perceptions are converted into informed and quantified problem definitions. The community is provided with a well-documented set of technical alternatives, sometimes with recommendations. The real engineers now get to deal with a more experienced community. The debate is informed.

However, as much of this chapter serves to indicate, introducing service-learning is not easy. Students have strong preconceptions about the nature of the civil engineering curriculum. Faculty are perhaps even more entrenched. We know that the body of human knowledge is doubling each decade. As we strive to prepare the next generation of civil engineers, faculty must struggle with the shape and bloating of the curriculum. The bewildering spread of new techniques puts stress on that curriculum. Our so-called "four-year-degree program" could become a 10-year program if all faculty initiatives were to be incorporated. So, when we are faced with yet another new demand for our overloaded curriculum (one that is not even technical), there is an understandable reluctance to show enthusiasm.

Conclusion

Engineering impacts us all. The University of Utah offers the community an independent source of engineering guidance and leadership. The university can serve as a vital bridge between that community and government agencies. The agents of this bridge are the students who apply their engineering expertise to real community concerns. The students learn that the technical component of their work is engineering design. They learn that their technical expertise is a service to their communities and that, for engineers, the actual design process should be exposed to public opinion. They learn, in a way that can never occur in a classroom, that they must communicate their skills to those they serve — the public. This means that their technical education acquires a new relevance. They work with real problems with real people. Furthermore, they begin to develop new skills.

Service-learning provides interactions with the community, facilitated through the presentation of reports to that community and through the participation of local groups in the assessment of student contributions. It enhances civic education by exposing students to the complex interaction between local groups and municipal authorities. It reduces students' reluctance to write by providing them with a real audience, one that needs to read and understand what they have written.

With the four components of the plan detailed in this paper, there exists a sound structural framework for curricular innovation. The application of these four key components in a sequential manner permits implementation of the plan through a structured 14-point mentoring guide. Together, the components and the guide find focus in an eight-stage implementation plan. All this has been presented as an example of how one engineering department is effecting change. Some of these ideas may be useful to others. Service-learning is too unusual for engineering faculty to accept without the help that only such a plan can provide. This plan, therefore, offers a route map for leaders and followers alike.

Selected Readings

American Society for Engineering Education. (October 1996). "Let Problems Drive the Learning in Your Classroom." *Prism – The Journal of the American Society for Engineering Education* 6(2): 30-36

Barber, B.R., and R.M. Battistoni. (June 1993). "A Season of Service: Introducing Service-Learning Into the Liberal Arts Curriculum." *PS: Political Science & Politics* 26(2): 235-240.

Bennion Center Faculty Advisory Committee. (October 1996). "Educating the Good Citizen for the Twenty-First Century: Service-Learning in Higher Education." Salt Lake City, UT: University of Utah.

Galura, J. (1993). *Praxis II: Service-Learning Resources for University Students, Staff and Faculty*. Ann Arbor, MI: OCSL Press.

Howard, J. (1993). *Praxis I: A Faculty Casebook on Community Service-Learning*. Ann Arbor, MI: OCSL Press.

Kraft, R.J., and M. Swadener, M., eds. (1994). *Building Community: Service Learning in the Academic Disciplines*. Denver, CO: Colorado Campus Compact.

Kupiec, T. (1994). *Rethinking Tradition: Integrating Service With Academic Study on College Campuses*. Providence, RI: Campus Compact.

Lieberman, T.M., and K. Connally. (1992). *Education and Action: A Guide to Integrating Classrooms and Communities*, 2nd. ed. St. Paul, MN: COOL Press.

Meisel, W., and R. Hackett. (1986). *Building a Movement: A Resource Book for Students in Community Service*. Minneapolis, MN: COOL Press.

Stanton, T. (1990). *Integrating Public Service With Academic Study: The Faculty Role*. Providence, RI: Campus Contact.

Wieckowski, T.J. (1992). "Student Community Service Programs: The Academic Connection." *NASPA Journal* 29(3): 207-212.

Professional Activism: Reconnecting Community, Campus, and Alumni Through Acts of Service

by Rand Decker

> *Professional: of or engaged in a profession (an occupation requiring advanced academic training, as medicine, law, etc.). . . .*
> *Activism: taking a direct action to achieve a political or social end. . . .*
>
> — *Webster's New World Dictionary*

Imagine: A dentist starts his workweek by filling his canceled appointments with children and adults in need of, but unable to pay for, dental care. These service recipients fill an otherwise unproductive gap in his professional schedule and consume only a small fraction of the resources of his busy practice. A single phone call from the dentist's receptionist to a campus-based community action center provides the link between those in need and his practice. These colleagues at the community action center know the dentist and his staff by their first names. In a matter of minutes our dentist has four appointments scheduled for this week. The university's community center will contact the dental care recipients. It was during his academic training that our dentist discovered both the magnitude of the need and the mechanisms that would help him professionally serve his community. Service-learning had been a big part of his college experience.

Now imagine again: This act of professional activism is replicated thousands of times a day in the offices and clinics of accountants, architects, attorneys, educators, engineers, health-care professionals, and social workers. These varied occupations are now linked by a common thread. A fraction of each professional's practice is set aside for acts of community service. Each maintains an ongoing, postgraduation, "provider-recipient brokerage" relationship to social needs and responsibilities illuminated by his or her service-learning experiences during academic training. In addition to the implicit, rejuvenating personal benefits of meeting a community need, these professionals are also rewarded with tax credits and recognition by professional societies as well as occupational and professional licensing boards. National calls to service and voluntarism no longer ask simply for your time. They ask for your most valuable time.

The arguments for institutionalized professional activism are so simple and compelling that they may have, to date, rendered the concept obscure. The powerful experiential teaching-learning environment of service-learning, coupled with that cadre of professionals who already have set aside a portion of their practice for community service, further inspires the concept.

A shift away from public-sector entitlements as the dominant mechanism for meeting our society's civic responsibilities has already begun. Filling the resulting void with an institutionalized, private-sector response is one of the only alternatives we have. Professional activism provides a means by which the great American economic engine can meet some of the needs of its disenfranchised population, and the neglected, underserved groups.

That we are generally predisposed toward the ideal of community service is clear. Three-fourths of all entering college freshmen have acted in a service or volunteer capacity during high school. Equally clear is we have been failing to nurture, let alone to institutionalize, this sense of civic responsibility as we move our students toward post-college careers. Only about one-half of those graduating have participated in service and volunteer activities during college (Astin 1996).

Service-learning addresses this failing and has thus become one of the most powerful tools available for integrating experiential teaching, professional training, and civic responsibility (and responsiveness) into higher education. Surveys of Campus Compact member institutions in 1998 indicate that among this group alone more than 575 institutions offer about 11,800 separate service-learning courses in all academic and professional disciplines.

Additionally, service-learning is being used successfully to address numerous, recognized shortcomings in the pedagogy of the science and engineering disciplines (Campus Compact 1996), including "graduates . . . ill-prepared to solve real problems in a cooperative way" (NSF 1996). Studies and reports have called on schools of engineering to "educate their students to work as part of teams, communicate well, and understand the economic, social, environmental, and international context of their professional activities" (ASEE 1994) and "to understand the impact of engineering solutions in a global and society context, a knowledge of contemporary issues, and an understanding of professional and ethical responsibility" (ABET 1998).

The service-learning experience, as well as the mechanism by which it is implemented on campuses, is microcosmic of institutionalized, postacademic, professional activism. In a service-learning environment, students who are training to become professionals master the learning objectives of the course against a recognized community need. That is, they are performing acts of professional activism as an element of their academic training. They are recognizing the need for and the value of those acts of service that they themselves can address with their growing professional skills.

Early indications are that, in addition to valuable learning, students derive a deep sense of personal benefit from their service-learning experiences. This being the case, we must also ask how we can continue to provide the mechanism for implementing professional activism in the postgraduate career workplace.

Herein lies the crucial role of campus-based community action centers. Campuses with successful service-learning programs invariably have an excellent community action center. The reason for this is not difficult to discover. One of the most challenging aspects of service-learning is matching a faculty member's course and learning objectives with a recognized community need. Not surprisingly, this same difficulty can be anticipated in the case of professionalism activism. However, at effective campus community action centers, the community's needs have already been canvassed. The community action centers then act as an intermediary or broker between those community needs and the service-learning faculty. They act to introduce and couple the service provider with the recipient. This role could easily be expanded to include brokering community needs with postgraduate alumni — alumni who, by virtue of the personal and institutional benefits that result, have chosen to set aside a portion of their practice for professional activism. In this way, we could address not only the needs of the community but also the epidemic disconnect between universities, their communities, and their alumni (Astin 1995; Boyer 1994; Cisneros 1995).

But how can professionals identify community need in the not unlikely event that they relocate away from their alma maters? The answer lies in the office or division most professional societies maintain to stay in touch with that profession's educational environment. Thus, if a professional were to relocate, he or she could simply call the local chapter of his or her professional society, and the latter, in turn, could put him or her in touch with the regional community action center that could best broker his or her professional activism with a recognized local community need.

Service-learning is here to stay. It is a sound, experiential pedagogy. It is imperative, however, that we regularly remind ourselves that service-learning is a means to an end, and not an end in itself. One of the many desired products of service-learning is a population of socially aware professionals who will set aside a portion of their practice to meet recognized community needs; that is, engage in acts of professional activism. To clarify further the issues discussed here, the relationship between service-learning, community need, campus-based community action centers, professional societies, public-sector agencies, and professional activism are depicted graphically in the figure that follows.

However, it must be stressed that implementing professional activism is not, at present, assured. It remains unclear whether professionals can be encouraged — by personal commitment, professional society and peer recognition, and privileges such as tax incentives — to set aside a portion of their practice to meet a recognized community need. Indeed, an engineer might develop a pilot study to test this question. Find a successful service-

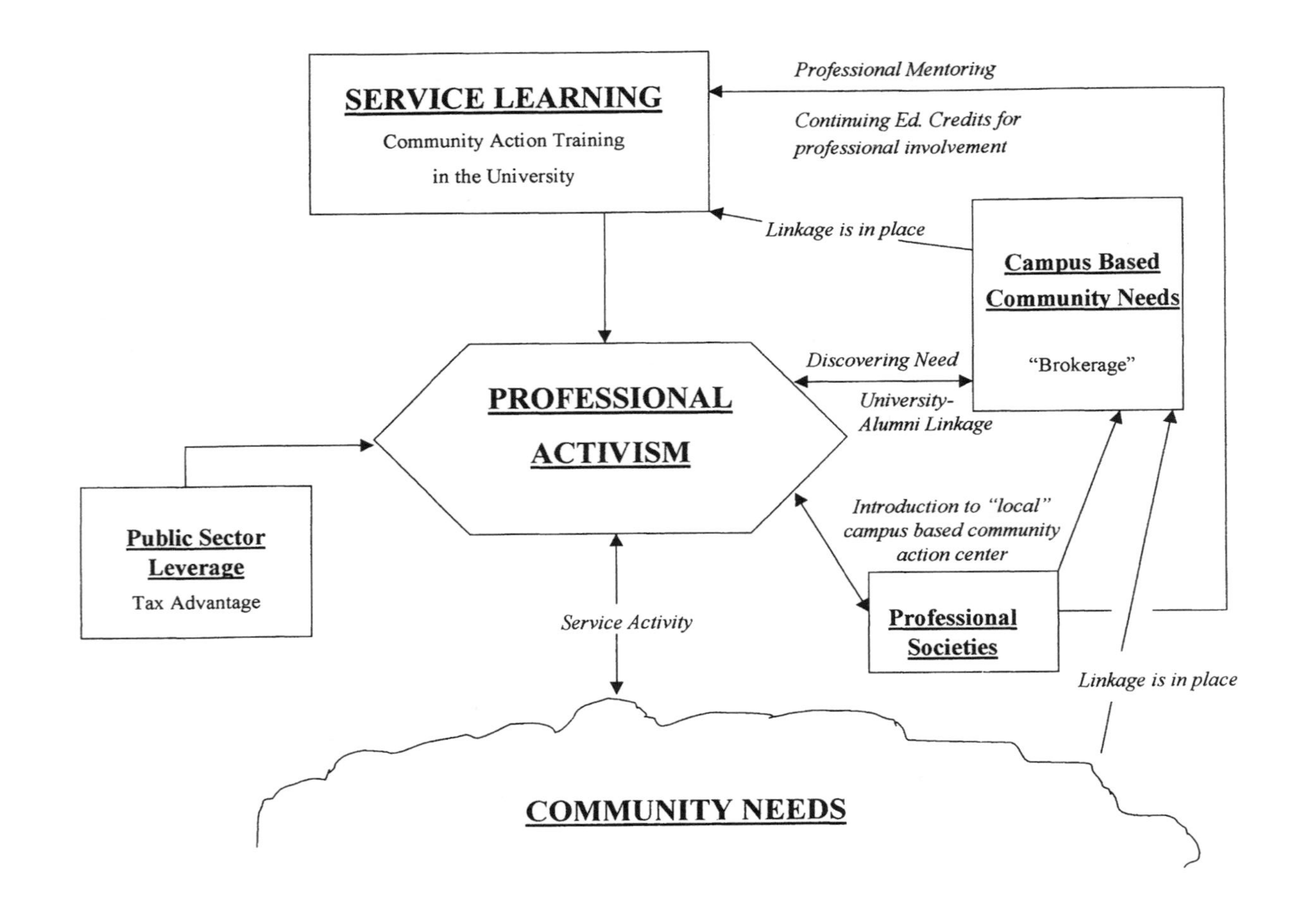
SERVICE LEARNING
Community Action Training
in the University
Professional Mentoring
Continuing Ed. Credits for
professional involvement
Linkage is in place
Campus Based
Community Needs
"Brokerage"
Discovering Need
University-
Alumni Linkage
PROFESSIONAL
ACTIVISM
Introduction to "local"
campus based community
action center
Public Sector
Leverage
Tax Advantage
Service Activity
Professional
Societies
Linkage is in place
COMMUNITY NEEDS

learning campus with a sound community action center and a cadre of post-graduate professionals willing to act as a test population. Create a linkage between the professionals and their alma mater's community center. Oversee the results, evaluate the costs and benefits, and study the case for lessons learned. A scientist might posit the null hypothesis: Busy professionals will never set aside a portion of their practices. And then prove it wrong. A skilled social scientist could examine the process of professional activism in detail.

Every professional needs to ask: What can I do, and what am I willing to do to bring the impact of service-learning to bear on community needs? How can I contribute to the development of an institutionalized mechanism to help facilitate the lifelong commitment of academically trained professionals to meet those needs? Truly, this is a question that deserves to be asked!

References

Accreditation Board for Engineering and Technology. (1998). *Engineering Criteria 2000.* Available on the ABET website at <http://www.abet.org>.

American Society for Engineering Education. (1994). *Engineering Education for a Changing World.* A joint project report of the Engineering Deans Council and the Corporate Roundtable of the ASEE. Available on the ASEE website at <http://www.asee.org>.

Astin, A.W. (1996). "The Role of Service-Learning in Higher Education." *About Campus* 1(1): 15-19.

———. (October 1995). "What Higher Education Can Do in the Cause of Citizenship." *The Chronicle of Higher Education,* B1-B2.

Boyer, E.L. (March 9, 1994). "Creating the New American College." *The Chronicle of Higher Education,* A48.

Campus Compact. (1996). "Science and Society: Redefining the Relationship." Providence, RI: Campus Compact.

Cisneros, H.G. (February 1995). "The University and the Urban Challenge." Washington, DC: U.S. Department of Housing and Urban Development.

National Science Foundation. (1996). "Shaping the Future: New Expectations for Undergraduate Education in Science, Mathematics, Engineering, and Technology." NSF report 96-139. Available from the NSF website at <http://www.nsf.gov>.

EPICS: Service-Learning by Design

by Edward J. Coyle and Leah H. Jamieson

Undergraduate students in engineering face a future in which they need more than just a solid technical background (ASEE 1994; Dahir 1993; Valenti 1996). In setting the goals for any system they are asked to design, they will be expected to communicate and work effectively with people of widely varying social and educational backgrounds. They will then be expected to work with people of many different technical backgrounds to achieve these goals. They thus need educational experiences that can help them develop the skills required by such expectations.

Community service agencies face a future in which they must rely to a great extent on technology for delivering, coordinating, improving, and accounting for the services they provide. They often possess neither the expertise nor the budget to design and acquire technological solutions suited to their missions. They thus need the help of people with strong technical backgrounds.

The Engineering Projects in Community Service (EPICS) program provides a service-learning structure that enables these two groups to work together and thereby satisfy each other's needs. This structure supports long-term projects in which teams of undergraduates in engineering are matched with community service agencies requesting technical assistance. Under the guidance of engineering faculty, the EPICS teams work closely with their agency partners over many years to define, design, build, and deploy the systems needed. The results are systems that have a significant, lasting impact on the community service agencies and the people they serve.

Origin and Design of the EPICS Program

The EPICS program (Coyle, Jamieson, and Dietz 1996; Coyle, Jamieson, and Sommers 1997) was initiated at Purdue University in the fall of 1995 to fulfill the complementary needs of engineering undergraduates and community service organizations as described above. It established a structured service-learning environment in which students experience realistic engineering design as a long-term, start-to-finish process. In the context of this experience, they develop the communication, teaming, and design skills now essential in the workplace. The EPICS program is thus well aligned with ABET 2000 criteria that reaffirm the importance of a broad view of what constitutes an engineering education.

The service aspects of the EPICS program contribute significantly to its success. Not only do they broaden students' perspective on and experience of society, they provide students with "customers" who truly want and will use the systems developed.

In the next three subsections we provide a broader discussion of the goals of the program, describe the unique ways in which it achieves these goals, and explain how it fits within the engineering curriculum at Purdue.

Goals and Unique Features of EPICS

Many of the goals of the EPICS program required the development of unique approaches to teaching design. These goals and the approaches they inspired include:

• **Emphasis on long-term design experience:** The EPICS track of courses spans freshman through senior year, with freshmen and sophomores registering for one credit per semester and juniors and seniors registering for one or two credits each semester. Thus, projects can last for many years and each student may participate in a project for up to seven semesters. This allows problems of significant scope and impact to be addressed. It also provides the students with sufficient time and a stable environment in which to develop critical nontechnical skills, such as teaming and communication skills.

• **Teams are vertically integrated:** Each team is a mix of freshmen, sophomores, juniors, and seniors. This vertically integrated composition, when combined with long-term registration of students for the same project, creates significant continuity in team membership from semester to semester and from year to year. As seniors on a team graduate, new freshmen and sophomores are added. Participating students can thus experience the team as new members during their first semester and then have the opportunity to grow into technical and organizational leadership positions by the time they graduate.

• **Projects are multidisciplinary:** Several current teams include electrical, computer, and mechanical engineering students as well as, in the case of two teams, sociology students. Students' disciplines, their academic "age," and their preferences regarding projects are the only data used when assigning them to EPICS teams.

• **Large project teams:** The large scope and long-term nature of these multidisciplinary projects require teams of 10-15 students. Such large teams provide their membership with significant organizational challenges in addition to providing them with the necessary number of minds and hands to complete large-scale projects.

• **Emphasis on start-to-finish experience:** EPICS involves students in a true define-design-build-test-deploy-support experience. They work with their partner organization to define the projects they will undertake and continue to interact with the organization through development, testing, deployment, and subsequent support of the fielded project.

- **Existence of a true customer:** Each team is paired with a local community organization to solve real problems. The fact that successful projects will actually be employed in the community creates a strong commitment from the individual students, the entire EPICS team, and the partner agency.

The above features of the EPICS program create an environment in which many critical career skills can be taught. Perhaps, most important, the students are provided with numerous opportunities, over an extended period of time, to hone these skills:

- **Communication:** EPICS projects require written reports, oral proposal and progress presentations, oral communications with sponsors and consultants, and intrateam communications.
- **Analytical thinking:** Because the scope and size of an EPICS project is much larger than is possible in traditional courses, students have to apply what they have learned to less well defined problems across a variety of disciplines.
- **Teamwork:** EPICS projects are large, so teamwork is essential. Students learn to divide up a large problem, assign and schedule subtasks, and integrate the pieces into a working solution.
- **Resourcefulness:** Vertically integrated projects encourage students to pursue nontraditional educational resources, such as their teammates, the project partner, and academic consultants who have experience related to the project.
- **Resource management:** Each team develops a proposal for the equipment and space requirements of the project, and has to take into account the resources of the sponsor.
- **Professional ethics:** Professional conduct, both in relation to the sponsor and within the team itself, is essential, so students must maintain an awareness of ethical principles while meeting the project demands.

Assessment Procedures

Independent formative and summative evaluations of the EPICS program have been conducted each semester by Professor J. William Asher, of Purdue's Educational Studies Department. In assessing the students' attitudes toward the program, the formative evaluations have been especially useful. A majority of the students cite the opportunity to obtain "practical, real-world experience in engineering design" as their primary reason for participating in the EPICS program. In every semester, however, a significant number of students also identify the opportunity to do community service as a major factor in their EPICS participation. Many of the students report that they have done community service in the past, through activities such as tutoring, church work, scouting, soup kitchens, crisis hot lines, and volunteer work for Habitat for Humanity. To date, none of the students has reported prior experience that combines community service with engineering.

To complement the descriptive evaluations, we have collected evaluation data along the dimensions of the specific program goals. To date, we have responses from 153 student evaluations, collected at the end of the spring 1996, fall 1996, and spring 1997 semesters. The students were asked,

> *Evaluate the impact that EPICS has had for you on each of the following: Your Technical Skills; Your Understanding of the Design Process; Your Communication Skills; Your Ability to Work on a Team; Your Resourcefulness; Your Organizational Skills; Your Awareness of the Community; Your Awareness of the "Customer" in an Engineering Project; Your Awareness of Ethical Issues.*

Each aspect was to be graded on a letter-grade scale of A (excellent) to F (poor), plus N/A (not applicable). In compiling the data, each A grade was assigned 4 points; each B, 3 points; and so on. Not included in the summary statistics were the 19 (out of 1,316) grades of N/A. The table on the next page shows the distribution, average, and standard deviation computed over three semesters.

In all aspects except technical skills, the students' average rating exceeded 3.0, which corresponds to a B. Since the emphasis in the early stages of a project is on problem definition and brainstorming of possible solutions rather than on implementation, it is not surprising that the impact on technical skills is rated lower than the other dimensions. Ability to work in a team and understanding of the design process received the highest scores. Community awareness received an average rating of 3.2.

EPICS in the Curriculum

The implementation of EPICS in the engineering curriculum is still evolving. It currently consists of a vertically integrated track of three courses in the School of Electrical and Computer Engineering. These courses have the permanent numbers EE-290, EE-390, and EE-490, for EPICS participation by sophomores, juniors, and seniors, respectively. In the spring of 1998, freshmen participated in most EPICS teams, thus completing the vertical integration of the program. The freshmen registered for ENGR-195B because all freshmen have a common first year.

ENGR-195B: The primary goal of this course is to provide second-

Student Responses to the Question: "Evaluate the Impact That EPICS Has Had for You on Each of the Following"

	Distribution of Scores (Points Earned)					Ave.	
	A(4)	B(3)	C(2)	D(1)	F(0)	Pts.	stdev
Technical skills	25	80	34	6	4	2.78	0.87
Understanding of the design process	58	44	6	0	1	3.45	0.68
Communication skills	71	66	14	1	0	3.36	0.67
Ability to work in a team	95	46	9	2	0	3.54	0.67
Resourcefulness	63	72	17	0	0	3.30	0.66
Organizational skills	47	81	21	3	0	3.13	0.71
Community awareness	63	56	28	3	0	3.19	0.81
Awareness of customer	81	53	14	1	1	3.41	0.74
Awareness of ethical issues	41	62	37	1	0	3.01	0.76

Note: Evaulation is on a 4-point scale with a rating of A corresponding to a 4.0.

semester freshmen with what is often their first glimpse of an engineering project. They attend all team meetings and all meetings between the team and its project partner. They are expected to learn their team's mission, become familiar with the nature and goals of the community service organization that is their team's project partner, and begin contributing to the team in any way they can. Because they are freshmen, they often — but not always — have limited technical skills. Their initial contributions thus usually take the form of assisting with the writing and editing of team reports and web pages, participating in brainstorming sessions, testing projects in the lab, providing support for projects that have been deployed in the field, and aiding in searches for team resources. Freshmen can register for ENGR-195B for one credit during their second semester.

EE-290: The objective here is to give sophomores further insight into the specific EPICS program they have joined and, more generally, into the design and development process. They, like the freshmen, attend planning and reporting meetings with the customer and all team meetings. Under the direction of the team's juniors and seniors, they perform and report on tasks consistent with their level of technical expertise. If they have joined the team as freshmen, they should already have learned enough — either on their own, or under the guidance of other team members — to begin making technical contributions. Sophomores can register in EE-290 for a total of two credits — one credit each semester.

EE-390: The responsibilities of the juniors in EE-390 include assisting the seniors in planning and organizing the project, solving technical problems, meeting with the customer, and supervising sophomores and freshmen. The juniors have principal responsibility for finding sources of information or technical expertise needed for the project. Each semester, a junior can register for either one or two credits of EE-390, with the number of credits being their choice.

EE-490: The seniors enrolled in EE-490 generally are responsible for the management tasks of planning and organizing their team's project activity and interacting with the faculty advisers and customer representatives. Their technical responsibilities include system design; solving technical problems; and training, monitoring, and directing the other team members in the tasks of system design, construction, testing, and deployment.

Students interested in EPICS are urged to enroll for at least two semesters in a row; otherwise, there is not sufficient time for them to fit into their team and make significant contributions. The goal is for students to join the program as early in their academic careers as possible and then continue with the program — working on the same project each semester — until they graduate. The results have been very gratifying: Of those students who can return each semester (i.e., they are not graduating, going on co-op, etc.),

74 percent do so.

Within the School of Electrical and Computer Engineering, three credits of EPICS in the senior year fulfill the senior design requirement for the BSEE degree or can be counted as one of the senior technical electives for the BSCmpE degree. An additional six EPICS credits can count toward the 46 required credits of ECE courses for the BSEE or BSCmpE degree. An unlimited number of EPICS credits can be counted as unrestricted electives. Engineering students from schools other than Electrical and Computer Engineering also register for EPICS by signing up for EE-290, 390, or 490. These courses count in their curricula as technical electives.

In the near future, we hope to have EPICS courses established within each school of engineering at Purdue. We expect this to occur first within the School of Mechanical Engineering, because approximately one-third of EPICS students are mechanical engineers. The remaining two-thirds are mostly students from Electrical and Computer Engineering, with a few students from the schools of Aeronautical, Chemical, and Civil Engineering.

Each student in the EPICS program attends a weekly two-hour meeting of his or her team in the EPICS laboratory and a one-hour lecture given each week for all EPICS students. These scheduled class and lab times ensure that students have a common time to meet. Additional meeting and work times are scheduled by the project team members.

The weekly one-hour lectures are usually given by guest experts and cover a wide range of topics. Lectures on communications and reporting have included topics such as proposal writing, technical presentations, collaborative report writing, creating World Wide Web documents, and visual design. Faculty members from the Krannert School of Management at Purdue have given presentations on project management, team dynamics, and a series of six lectures (two per semester) on ethics. The students have participated in a diversity workshop run by Purdue's Office of Diversity and Multicultural Affairs. A series of lectures on entrepreneurship has brought in speakers from local start-up companies and the founder of a national engineering company, as well as speakers from the Krannert School of Management, Purdue's Office of Industrial Relations and Office of Technology Transfer, the director of the local Business and Industrial Development Center, and the city attorney for the City of Lafayette. Purdue engineering faculty and staff have made presentations on the design process and product safety as well as on technical topics relevant to several of the teams. The executive director of United Way of Tippecanoe County has also met with the EPICS students.

Implementing EPICS: Projects and Project Partners

Each EPICS project involves a team of eight to 12 undergraduates, one or more community service agencies, and a faculty adviser. As has been noted, each team is vertically integrated, consisting of a mix of sophomores, juniors, and seniors. Each team is constituted for several years — from initial project definition through final deployment —- with students participating for several semesters. This structure makes possible long-term projects. Over time, each project has five phases: finding project partners, assembling a project team, project proposal, system design and development, and system deployment and support.

Phase 1: Finding Project Partners

Each EPICS project addresses the technology-based problems of one or more local community service organizations. Agencies with appropriate problems must, therefore, be found.

When planning for the EPICS program first started in the fall of 1994, we were able to contact many service agencies at the same time by making a presentation about the program and its goals at the monthly meeting of the directors of all local United Way agencies. This single presentation led to many discussions with individual agencies and a long list of potential projects.

From this list of potential projects, those best suited for the EPICS program were selected. Projects are selected based on their:

- **Significance:** There are a large number of potential EPICS projects within a city the size of Lafayette, IN, which has a population of approximately 100,000. It is not possible for us to pursue all of them, so those that should provide the greatest benefit to the community are selected.
- **Level of technology:** Projects must be challenging to, but within the capabilities of, undergraduates in engineering.
- **Expected duration:** Although projects might have components that can be completed in a semester, each project must be long-term, requiring two or more years of effort from a team of 10 to 15 undergraduates.

Since the first round of projects grew out of the presentation at United Way, the source of new projects has been varied. Some projects have been initiated by faculty; others have been suggested by students. As the program has become known in the community, several projects have been proposed by community service organizations themselves. Each year, new projects are selected by the EPICS faculty, using the significance, level of technology, and expected duration criteria. From five initial projects in Fall 1995, the program has grown to seven projects in Fall 1996 and to 12 in Fall 1997. Those 12 projects are summarized at the end of this article.

Phase 2: Assembling a Project Team

Once a project and project partner have been identified, a student team is organized. This is done by advertising the project in undergraduate classes and on the World Wide Web. Eight to 12 students are chosen for each project team. Depending on the needs of the project partner, teams might reflect a single engineering discipline or be multidisciplinary, including students from two or more engineering fields.

The team must be vertically integrated: It must consist of a mix of sophomores, juniors, and seniors. Each student is requested to participate in the project for as many semesters as possible. The combination of a vertically integrated team and long-term student participation ensures continuity in projects from semester to semester and year to year. Projects can thus last many years if new students, especially freshmen and sophomores, are recruited for the project as team members graduate.

Phase 3: The Project Proposal

During the first semester of a project, the project team meets several times with its project partner and the EPICS faculty to define the project and determine its goals. During this phase, the project team learns about the mission, needs, and priorities of the project partner. A key aspect of this phase is identifying projects that satisfy three criteria: They are needed by the project partner; they require engineering design; and they are a reasonable match for the team's capabilities. Also, to ensure that the students build confidence and the project partners see progress, the teams are encouraged to pursue a mix of long-term and short-term objectives. Short-term projects generally require only one or two semesters to complete; long-term projects take two or more years. This process of project definition culminates in a written proposal and presentation in the fourth week of the semester. The proposal is critiqued during a lab session, with detailed feedback provided in the areas of organization, content, technical approach, and writing. The proposal must be approved by the EPICS faculty and then be accepted by the project partner.

Phase 4: System Design and Development

Starting from week five of the first semester of a project, the project team's goal is to produce a prototype of the hardware and software systems discussed in the proposal. Interaction with the project partner continues, to ensure that the systems being designed and developed are as desired. The formal portion of this interaction takes the form of a written progress report and an oral presentation delivered by the project team to the EPICS faculty and the project partner at the middle and end of each semester. These progress reports must meet the same standards as the proposals do. The project team demonstrates the current state of its systems to a team of EPICS faculty every five weeks for the duration of the project.

Phase 4 lasts as many semesters as is necessary for the team to complete the project to the satisfaction of the project partner.

Phase 5: System Deployment and Support

The ultimate goal of each project team is to deliver a system to the project partner. After fielding a prototype, the team must train the agency's representatives to use the system, collect feedback, and make any reasonable changes requested by the partner. One of the hallmarks of the EPICS program is that the systems designed and built by the students are deployed in the field, where they provide real, needed service to the community.

Once an EPICS team has deployed a system and provided sufficient training for agency staff, the project is in principle over. We have yet to see this occur, however, because the EPICS teams are often working on several systems at any one time, and ideas for additional systems or improving currently deployed systems are constantly being generated. We do not envision any of the 12 current EPICS projects ending in the next few years. Thus, the EPICS teams exhibit a key characteristic of corporations: They continue to generate new or improved projects and to branch out into new markets.

Results

The seven EPICS teams that have been in operation for a year or longer have already deployed a substantial number of systems to, or provided substantive services for, their agency partners. To detail here these systems and services is not possible due to lack of space. Thus, we provide below an abbreviated list, and ask interested readers to consult the EPICS website (http://www.ecn.purdue.edu/epics) for more details.

All EPICS projects are very ambitious in scale and hence require substantial time to produce systems that can be delivered in the field. The deliverables described opposite were all produced between the fall of 1995 and the fall of 1997 — in other words, in less than two years.

One of the delivered systems — the remote control lock that is custom-designed for school lockers — has commercial potential. An EPICS student has formed a small company to make the 30 locks ordered by the Greater Lafayette Area Special Services to aid the students it serves in several schools in Lafayette. This type of remote-controlled lock might one day be available for disabled students throughout the country. It represents an excellent example of the impact that the EPICS program can have.

Systems Delivered and Services Provided by EPICS Teams

Children's Clinic at Wabash Center -- ECE Emphasis: Doll house kitchen with electronically controlled refrigerator door, lights, and kitchen sounds activated by a child via a large, easy-to-use touch pad.

Children's Clinic at Wabash Center -- ME Emphasis: A four-button phone adapted for children with physical disabilities. The structure and controls of a commercially available electric car were modified to allow safe use indoors and to provide better back support.

Habitat for Humanity: New design for construction of corners that minimizes air leakage; brochure for homeowners describing ways to save energy through proper choice of light bulbs and how to compute the expected savings; thermal imaging of houses to determine their energy efficiency.

Home Healthcare Services: Several improvements, including email and automated file backup, made to the agency's computer network; system designed to enable network-wide access to the agency's printer; field-testing of first prototype of nurse scheduling software, with much improved second version nearly completed.

Homelessness Prevention Network: Computers with stand-alone databases delivered to six agencies for their use over the last six months. Central server and its software have been developed and are currently being tested in the lab.

Lafayette Crisis Center: First prototype of kiosk developed and field-tested; second prototype nearly finished. Kiosk automatically updates its local database each night from the official database at the Lafayette Crisis Center. Kiosk can connect users to any community service organization via an automatically dialed phone.

Speech-Language and Audiology Clinics: Software for counting the number of syllables in spoken dialogue completed and tested; real-time implementation on special-purpose hardware under way. Infrared-controlled lock installed at local middle school for a physically disabled student. Tracheal model to assist laryngectomy patients in use. Several versions of voice-interactive children's software in use.

References

American Society for Engineering Education. (1994). *Engineering Education for a Changing World.* A joint project report of the Engineering Deans Council and the Corporate Roundtable of the ASEE. Available on the ASEE website at <http://www.asee.org>.

Coyle, E.J., L.H. Jamieson, and H.G. Dietz. (June 1996). "Long-Term Community Service Projects in the Purdue Engineering Curriculum." Paper presented at the 1996 Annual ASEE Conference, Anaheim, CA.

Coyle, E.J., L.H. Jamieson, and L.S. Sommers. (Fall 1997). "EPICS: A Model for Integrating Service-Learning Into the Engineering Curriculum." *Michigan Journal of Community Service-Learning* 4: 81-89.

Dahir, M. (August/September 1993). "Educating Engineers for the Real World." *Technology Review* 96(6): 14-16.

Valenti, M. (July 1996). "Teaching Tomorrow's Engineers." *Mechanical Engineering Magazine* 118(7): 64-69.

Acknowledgment

This work is supported in part by the U.S. Department of Education's Fund for the Improvement of Postsecondary Education under grant P116F50129, by the National Science Foundation's Instrumentation and Laboratory Improvement Program under grant DUE96-50771, and by the Corporation for National Service's Learn and Serve America Higher Education Program under grant 97LHEIN025.

Summary of Fall 1997 EPICS Projects

1. **Title**: Children's Clinic at Wabash Center - ECE Emphasis.
   Project Partner: The Wabash Center Children's Services.
   Facts: Begun in Fall 1995; 7 ECEs, 1 IDE, and 3 MEs on Fall 97 team.
   Tasks: Develop computer-controlled toys for children with physical disabilities. Develop an artificial sensory environment to provide multi-sensory stimulation and a sense of control to children with physical disabilities.
   Technologies: Motors, electronics, computer controls.
   Impact: Expanded capabilities and control of their environment for children with physical disabilities.

2. **Title**: Children's Clinic at Wabash Center - ME Emphasis.
   Project Partner: The Wabash Center Children's Services.
   Facts: Begun in Fall 1996; 3 ECEs, 5 MEs, and 1 MSE on Fall 97 team.
   Tasks: Develop electro-mechanical toys and play areas for children with physical disabilities. Provide ways for physically disabled children to control their motion and to play with their peers.
   Technologies: Structures, actuators, ergonomics, safety.
   Impact: Improved methods for encouraging physically disabled children to develop socially and to develop their sense of motion.

3. **Title**: Habitat for Humanity.
   Project Partner: The Greater Lafayette Chapter of Habitat for Humanity.
   Facts: Begun in Fall 1996; 7 ECEs, 1 CE, 1 ChE, 1 IE and 2 MEs on Fall 97 team.
   Tasks: Design systems and structures to minimize home construction and energy costs. Develop new construction techniques and investigate new construction materials..
   Technologies: Power electronics, solar cells, heat flow, materials, energy efficient structures.
   Impact: Lower-cost houses and lower home operating expenses for the working poor.

4. **Title**: Home Healthcare Services.
   Project Partner: The Visiting Nurse Home Health Service.
   Facts: Begun in Fall 1995; 10 ECEs on Fall 97 team.
   Tasks: Develop software to manage nurse scheduling and point of care service. Design and build RF-controlled locks and appliance controls to enable home- and bed-bound patients to control their houses.
   Technologies: Scheduling algorithms, databases, wireless remote control, electro-mechanical systems.
   Impact: More efficient use of agency personnel; new capabilities to help patients.

5. **Title**: Homelessness Prevention Network.
   Project Partner: Eight Agencies of the Tippecanoe County Homelessness Prevention Network.
   Facts: Begun in Fall 1995; 11 ECEs and 3 Sociologists on Fall 97 team.
   Tasks: Design and implement a centralized database that allows the agencies to coordinate their services, track their clients, and assemble accurate reports without violating clients' confidentiality.
   Technologies: Databases, cryptography, communication, software.
   Impact: Improved coordination of agencies serving the homeless; more accurate understanding and reporting of the scope of homelessness in Tippecanoe County, Indiana.

6. **Title**: Imagination Station/Burtsfield Elementary School.
   Project Partner: Imagination Station (an interactive science and space museum) and Burtsfield Elementary School.
   Facts: Begun in Fall 1997; 5 ECEs and 5 MEs on Fall 97 team.
   Tasks: Develop systems to aid in science, mathematics and technology education.
   Technologies: Networked multi-media systems, human-computer interfaces, video technology.
   Impact: Improved educational resources for the community.

7. **Title**: Indiana Division of Families and Children.
   Project Partner: The four service agencies comprising Alternative Community-Based Services.
   Facts: Begun in Fall 1997; 10 ECEs, 1 ME, and 2 Sociologists on Fall 97 team.
   Tasks: Develop a centralized database to help the four service agencies coordinate their activities and share information. Develop custom palm-top software to aid service personnel visiting families.
   Technologies: Databases, cryptography, communication, software.
   Impact: Improved and less-expensive social services for at-risk children and their families.

8. **Title**: Klondike Elementary School.
   Project Partner: Klondike Elementary School.
   Facts: Begun in Fall 1997; 9 ECEs and 3 MEs on Fall 97 team.
   Tasks: Design of custom educational software, sound systems, and multimedia tools for education.
   Technologies: Acoustics, electronics, software.
   Impact: Improved educational environment.

9. **Title**: Lafayette Crisis Center.
   Project Partner: Lafayette Crisis Center.
   Facts: Begun in Fall 1995; 8 ECEs and 2 MEs on Fall 97 team.
   Tasks: Design stand-alone kiosks that will provide information about community services to people in need of assistance. Incorporate means of contacting appropriate agencies.
   Technologies: Databases, human-computer interfaces, weather-proof enclosures, touch-screens.
   Impact: Improved access to community services.

10. **Title**: Office of the Dean of Students.
    Project Partner: Purdue University's Office of the Dean of Students.
    Facts: Begun in Fall 1997; 4 ECEs and 8 MEs on Fall 97 team.
    Tasks: Design classroom furniture for physically handicapped college students; develop closed-captioning systems for deaf and hard-of-hearing college students.
    Technologies: Structures, closed-captioning systems, ergonomics, mechanics.
    Impact: Improved access to education for physically disabled and hard-of-hearing students.

11. **Title**: Speech-Language and Audiology Clinics.
    Project Partner: The M. D. Steer Audiology and Speech-Language Center.
    Facts: Begun in Fall 1995; 7 ECEs and 2 MEs on Fall 97 team.
    Tasks: Automate calculation of speech rate for clinical sessions. Design specialized speech recognition systems. Design directional microphone system for hearing aids.
    Technologies: Speech synthesis and recognition, human-computer interfaces.
    Impact: New services for the clinic's clients; improved feedback on effects of therapy.

12. **Title**: Tippecanoe County Historical Association.
    Project Partner: The Tippecanoe County Historical Association.
    Facts: Begun in Fall 1997; 9 ECEs and 2 MEs on Fall 97 team.
    Tasks: Develop multi-media and electro-mechanical systems for on-line storage and interactive presentation of historical information.
    Technologies: Video/image processing, image database management, virtual reality.
    Impact: Enhanced access to and use of historical archives and sites.

Service-Learning in a Variety of Engineering Courses

by John Duffy

This chapter represents a case study in why and how service-learning was introduced into several engineering courses. The approaches described here might be useful to others who plan to employ service-learning in their courses. The chapter also presents a poll of student opinions. It begins with a brief consideration of the basic what, why, and how of service-learning in engineering.

What Is Service-Learning?

Service-learning has been defined as "a form of experiential education in which students engage in activities that address human and community needs together with structured opportunities intentionally designed to promote student learning and development. Reciprocity and reflection are key concepts of service-learning" (Jacoby and Associates 1996: 5). Service-learning has a two-fold focus: learning for the student and service to the community.

There are 10 principles of good practice in combining service and learning, according to the National Society for Experiential Education (Honnet and Poulsen 1989). These include "an effective and sustained program that"

- engages people in responsible and challenging actions for the common good;
- allows for those with needs to define those needs;
- provides structured opportunities for people to reflect critically on the service experience; and
- includes training, supervision, monitoring, support, recognition, and evaluation (13-16).

Why Service-Learning?

The approach of service-learning is consistent with the theories and empirical research of a number of leading educators and developmental psychologists, including Dewey, Piaget, Kolb, Kohlberg, Perry, Belenky et al., Baxter Magolda, and Coles (see Brandenberger 1998 and references in Jacoby and Associates 1996). The approach is also consistent with the recent change in paradigm in education from a focus on teaching to a focus on learning (Barr and Tagg 1995; Johnson, Johnson, and Smith 1991). Astin, Sax, and Avalos

(1998), in extensive surveys of thousands of college students over a number of years, found service to be beneficial in retention, in community service after graduation, in racial interaction, in civic responsibility, and in development of a meaningful philosophy of life. Positive cognitive and attitude development is expected of students involved in service-learning.

Recently Eyler and Giles (1999) questioned 1,500 students from 20 colleges/universities in a study of the effect of service-learning. Service-learning was found to impact positively tolerance, personal development, interpersonal development, and community and college connections. Students reported working harder, being more curious, connected learning to personal experience, and demonstrated deeper understanding of subject matter. The quality of placements in the community and the degree of structured reflection were found to be important in enhancing these positive effects, significantly so for critical thinking. The authors summed up effective service-learning principles in five C's: *connection* (students, peers, community, faculty; experience and analysis); *continuity* (all four years; reflection before, during, after service); *context* (messiness of community setting is integral to learning); *challenge* (to current perspectives; not overwhelming); and *coaching* (opportunity for interaction; emotional, intellectual support).

Why Service-Learning in Engineering?

The Accreditation Board for Engineering and Technology (ABET 1998) has issued a new set of criteria for engineering programs. In addition to more traditional technical issues, the new criteria include the demand that graduates demonstrate:

- an ability to function on multidisciplinary teams;
- an understanding of professional and ethical responsibility;
- an ability to communicate effectively;
- a broad education necessary to understand the impact of engineering solutions in global and societal contexts;
- a recognition of the need for, and an ability to engage in, lifelong learning; and
- a knowledge of contemporary issues.

It appears that service-learning team projects have the potential to ensure that students learn and demonstrate these qualities as well as the ability to apply engineering to the design and analysis of systems and experiments.

How to fit more material into an already packed curriculum is, of course, a continuing challenge to engineering educators and students. However, service-learning might itself offer a way to integrate activities designed to strengthen abilities in technical areas with otherwise discrete efforts focused on the development of nontechnical competencies. As other chapters in this volume indicate, service-learning has been integrated into a variety of engineering courses, particularly capstone design courses and directed studies. For example, Purdue's EPICS program model (see chapter by Coyle and Jamieson) has now been adopted at Notre Dame and Iowa State. The University of Utah, well represented in this volume, has a variety of engineering courses involving service-learning. Other schools, such as Colorado State University, have established service-learning programs in engineering (see Campus Compact documents and website: www.compact.org). However, compared with the 11,800 service-learning courses reported by 575 member campuses of Campus Compact (1998 survey reported in Eyler and Giles 1999), service-learning in engineering still has a way to go before it is on a par with analogous work in other disciplinary areas.

How Were Projects Set Up?

At the University of Massachusetts-Lowell (UML), I am responsible for three graduate courses in solar engineering, one graduate course in manufacturing systems, two undergraduate courses in laboratory methods, and one capstone design course. Just as I was trying to think of a way to incorporate service into these courses, I found out that the university's Office of Community Service was trying to organize a student chapter of Habitat for Humanity. The proverbial light went on! Later, after designing service projects in conjunction with Habitat for Humanity, I also began designing projects with communities in Peru. Most recently, I have collaborated with AmeriCorps volunteers and several neighborhood groups in Lowell. Before I turn to the actual projects, however, a few contextual clarifications are in order.

Habitat for Humanity International is an organization "dedicated to eliminating substandard housing and homelessness worldwide and to making adequate, affordable shelter a matter of conscience and action. Habitat has built more than 65,000 houses around the world, providing more than 300,000 people with safe, decent, affordable shelter" (Habitat 1998). Since 1987, more than 500 campus chapters have been formed in several countries.

Affordable, comfortable housing is particularly needed in the city of Lowell, which has high unemployment and a low average income. In addition, the Lowell community needs to be educated as to the potential of passive solar systems and energy-conservation techniques in new and retrofitted housing. To meet this educational need, service-learning projects were incorporated into several engineering courses. The goal was to increase both student and community understanding of solar energy through initiatives focusing on the design and testing of solar and energy-efficient features in Habitat housing located near the university. It was only logical that

I should contact the Habitat for Humanity of Greater Lowell to discuss my interests and the community's needs.

After succeeding in integrating Habitat projects into several courses, I looked for new community links and undertakings. Several possibilities presented themselves: One concerned the water quality of local rivers; another, refrigeration, lights, and radio communication in remote medical clinics in the Sierra of Peru.

The Peru project originated in a trip made by the university chaplain and several undergraduates during the summer of 1997. The group traveled to mountain villages in Peru to visit descendants of the Quechua people, for the most part subsistence farmers sharing land and other resources. Most of these villages have no electricity and no running water; the people live in mud adobe houses. When the natives asked their visitors for vaccine refrigerators, radio communication, and lights for the town medical clinics, the visitors turned to the College of Engineering for assistance. In the summer of 1998 and in January 1999, I and several graduate students in the college's solar engineering program designed and installed photovoltaic/battery systems in the clinics of five villages. Of the eight students who went to Peru to install the systems, three were undergraduates from universities other than UML.

MASSPIRG (Massachusetts Public Interest Research Group) provided the key link to the river improvement project. In searching for an appropriate community undertaking for the first of two mechanical engineering lab courses I teach, I contacted the campus MASSPIRG office and was informed that AmeriCorps workers had begun a river cleanup project at the request of local neighborhood groups. Since one of the goals of the lab course is uncertainty analysis, an experiment involving river sampling for water quality including uncertainty analysis of the results seemed a good fit for the course and the community. Clearly one of the lessons of my experience is that those wishing to start service-learning projects should look to existing campus organizations as one way to establish valuable community contacts efficiently.

Would the Students Accept Service-Learning?

The students at UML are mostly commuters, with only 10 percent of the undergraduates coming from out of state. A questionnaire I had devised was distributed to all the classes in which I hoped to introduce service-learning. Basic information was solicited about age, course loads, workloads, time spent volunteering, and general sociological attitudes. (The details of this questionnaire are presented later in this chapter.) The 28 responses in one undergraduate class were typical: Students worked an average of 16 hours weekly during the semester (with a range of 0 to 53 hours), with most students also taking a full academic load (15 semester credit hours). Their average age was 26. The number of hours they volunteered was low, approximately three per month. It appeared that some of our students might have been just beyond the need of service themselves!

One obvious challenge was to ensure that the service-learning component in these courses did not entail any additional time from student schedules or create a financial burden for them. Furthermore, scheduling group work always presents challenges for commuter students. Challenges such as these had to be met without weakening academic course content in any way.

Student attitudes toward integrating service with academic coursework were on average slightly positive, but several students strongly disagreed with the notion (13 percent). I presented the community-based work to my classes in a rather straightforward manner, since it has been my experience that overly emotional motivational speeches don't appeal to engineering students.

Although the students who went on the trips to Peru did not receive academic credit for their work, they certainly were involved in service-learning. In fact, one graduate student liked the work so much, she accepted a position to do similar work with indigenous mountain farmers in her native country. The Peru project is still ongoing, and now provides challenging systems for undergraduate and graduate design courses, as described in the following section, and for master's theses.

What Were the Expected Outcomes?

The expected outcomes for students included:

• sufficient knowledge of the subject matter in respective courses to solve real-world problems;

• enhanced motivation, active learning, and experience with serving and caring for others in the community, while covering the same course material as previously;

• more practical application of engineering principles covered in the courses;

• sensitivity to the sociological and environmental consequences of engineering decisions through community interaction;

• application of "good engineering practice" by treating the community participants as "customers" to achieve quality improvement; and

• in general, all the positive cognitive and affective benefits found in previous studies.

The expected outcomes for the communities involved included:

• more energy-efficient, affordable, comfortable, sustainable housing;

• lighting, vaccine refrigeration, and communication for remote mountain clinics;

• the realization that energy conservation and solar systems work effectively;

• the transfer of knowledge and skills related to solar system design and construction to local groups and perhaps beyond to other groups in similar climates.

The expected outcomes for the university included:

• increased economic and social benefit to the region, which is in the charter of the university;

• improved community relations;

• increased retention of students; and

• graduates with more civic responsibility.

Courses and Projects

I incorporated service-learning into seven engineering courses at different academic levels with the goal of increasing both student and community understanding of various aspects of engineering. Descriptions of the seven courses and the associated projects follow. The content-related learning objectives of each course are given along with its related service aspects. In every instance, the students produced written reports on their projects, which by their nature contained reflections on the service activities. The reports were given to community group representatives.

Solar Systems Engineering

A Habitat miniproject was initiated during the spring of 1997 in a solar systems engineering class. Students analyzed the effect of different windows and insulation levels on the energy efficiency of a local Habitat house being rebuilt at the time. Part of the curriculum of this course involves determining the heat-loss-coefficient-area product (UA) of a building that can be modeled as a single zone and also estimating the net energy from south-facing windows of buildings. Students took measurements at the house at the start of the project and at completion of their analysis. Habitat followed their suggestions wherever possible, particularly with regard to floor insulation, a factor that Habitat had not included in its house rehab projects up until this time.

A miniproject in the spring of 1998 had the students design the thermal features of a new house, five copies of which Habitat plans to build soon on one large parcel of donated land. The new model is to have a footprint of about 600 square feet and a total floor area of no more than 1,300 square feet, so units can fit on relatively small lots. The students specified rough floor plans, significant passive solar features, levels of insulation, types of windows; estimated seasonal energy performance; and predicted the cost-benefit of the features for a typical house. All these activities correspond to learning objectives of the course. (The actual instructions given to the students are reproduced at the end of the chapter.)

Mechanical Engineering Capstone Design

A project developed for a six-credit mechanical engineering capstone course involved helping to design a new Habitat house. The overall purpose of the capstone course is to provide a context for students to apply principles and skills learned in previous courses. One team of students chose to produce a more detailed design and analysis of the new Habitat house described above. The target energy performance was a utility bill for space heating of less than $250 per season. The students met with the Habitat construction crew and a local architect to get feedback and exchange ideas.

As a result of this project, students not only designed the thermal features of the house but also laid out the floor plans, sized the main structural beams and posts, and performed a life-cycle cost-benefit analysis. The auxiliary space heating is predicted to cost only $55 per year for natural gas. The extra $5,000 in materials required for such a superinsulated passive solar house with small sunspace is expected to be paid back in less than nine years. Even with the extra mortgage payments, the homeowners will be saving about $250 a year. Habitat personnel attended the students' final presentation for the course. The Habitat Building Committee accepted the team's findings with great interest and appreciation.

In the spring of 1999 two sets of students worked on designs for the Peru project. The previous summer, the medical technicians in the Peruvian village of Malvas asked us whether we could provide a device to make ice so that vaccines could be kept cold in a thermos. (Certain vaccines are ruined if they get above 8° C.) The vaccines could then be taken on trips to even more remote areas. Two students (one of whom is actually from Lima) designed a solid-state icemaker capable of running off a solar system. They also built and tested a prototype.

A pervasive problem in remote areas of the world is a supply of clean water. The villages in the mountains of Peru typically have spring water, which may look clean but is of unknown purity. Three capstone students designed a pasteurization system with a solar hot water collector and an automatic device to ensure the water stays at a minimum of 150° F for a minimum of six minutes. A prototype was built and tested. The system will be built in Peru out of local materials and installed in the village of Huayan by two of its three student designers.

Mechanical Engineering Lab II

In the fall of 1997 and the summer and fall of 1998, five minidesign projects were created for seniors, organized into five teams, in a mechanical engineering laboratory methods/statistics course involving Habitat house measurements. They were: blower door test for leakiness, daylighting/lighting test, original wood strength test, coheat test to estimate the heat loss coefficient, and tracer gas infiltration test. The learning objectives in this two-semester course typically include selection of sensors, design of experiments, and hypothesis testing, and it was a challenge meeting these objectives while incorporating a service component. (The actual instructions given to the students are reproduced at the end of the chapter.) Students did, however, actually carry out the tests they designed at one of the houses being rehabilitated.

Of special interest were the results of an experiment comparing the compressive and bending strengths of the wood samples. The old wood was on average better than the new, with statistically significant differences for the yield point under compression. In the summer of 1998, a second class, basing its work on the results of the first group but using more samples, also found the old wood significantly stronger when bent. The Habitat crew was delighted with these results, which eased their concerns about the safety of older structures.

Solar Engineering Fundamentals

In the fall of 1997, in a graduate solar engineering fundamentals course, a miniproject was developed to analyze solar access on a site for yet another new Habitat house and to estimate solar gain through the proposed sunspace windows. The curriculum of this course contains subjects such as sun angles, shading evaluation, transmittance, and absorptance. The results of the student analysis indicated that the site, which at first did not seem suitable for passive solar due to the nature of several surrounding buildings, would indeed run little risk of excessive shading if the proposed house were positioned on the lot in a manner consistent with the placement of neighboring houses.

Manufacturing Systems

In a graduate course on manufacturing systems, topics such as stochastic systems, queuing theory, reliability, and linear programming are covered. In the fall of 1998 I introduced into the course a minimal service-learning component in the form of extra credit miniprojects. These were related to our Peru project: reliability testing and analysis of portable lantern switches that had failed in Peru, and stochastic model development of the PV/battery system used in Malvas for use in improved designs elsewhere. (See the material reproduced at the end of the chapter for details.) Some typical features of service-learning, such as direct reciprocity, were not present in these miniprojects, although one of the 12 students in the course had been to Peru twice with us. I anticipate expanding the service-learning component of this course to include more of those features.

Mechanical Engineering Laboratory I

In the first of the two-part ME laboratory/statistics course sequence, I introduced, in the spring of 1999, a final experiment on uncertainty analysis involving field measurements and a service-learning component. The WaterWatch program on campus needed help in analyzing the water quality of a small river in Lowell in response to neighbors' requests. I had each of four student sections measure the flow, temperature, acidity, and dissolved oxygen content of the stream. They were then asked to estimate flow-weighted averages of the last three parameters, report the results to the community on posters for an Earth Day Fair, and estimate the quantitative uncertainty (95 percent confidence limits) of each parameter average. (Detailed instructions are reproduced at the end of the chapter.) As in the case of the manufacturing systems miniprojects, the reciprocity aspect of the work in this course was somewhat limited, though the community did learn that there were no alarming water quality parameters at the time of sampling. For their part, the students learned how to perform field measurements in a "messy" environment and how to estimate the accuracy of their results. From the community they learned that the rivers in the town do need some attention in the form of debris removal. Future work will increase the opportunity for the students to learn more directly from the community.

Energy Design Workshop

The energy design course in our energy engineering master's degree program is similar in concept to the capstone design course for undergraduates. In the spring of 1999 a project arose in conjunction with a request from a missionary house in a coastal town in Peru. The water there is heated by electricity, and the utility bills were getting more expensive. However, funds not used for house utilities could go toward other purposes; for example, for seeds for farmers. The course project involved design of a solar hot water system utilizing materials available in Peru and an analysis for the cost-benefits of the system. Once the design was completed, the components were, in fact, ordered, and a group arranged to go to Peru to install the system with the help of a local technician.

In the spring of 1998, three students designed improvements in a solar coffee dryer design in cooperation with a local nonprofit company started by two former students and one current student. The coffee dryers are intended not only to provide an alternative to cutting and burning forests in Latin America but also to provide more income to local farmers, who get more for dried coffee beans. Prototype subsystems were manufactured and tested, and students have actually helped install and test the dryers in Costa Rica.

Thesis Projects

Several MS and DSc theses in solar engineering at UML have involved service-learning. Topics have included a rural solar electrification startup company in India (now with more than 2,500 PV installations), solar crop dryers in Costa Rica, and PV rural home electrification monitoring system design and implementation in the Dominican Republic. Some of this work is reported in Duffy et al. (1999), Hande, Martin, and Duffy (1998), Raudales et al. (1998), and Duffy (1998).

Summary of Service-Learning Components in Several Courses

The service-learning components of the seven courses have varied considerably in extent. Some service projects have replaced assignments and projects previously related to nonservice applications. (See the summary table opposite.)

Improvements in the design of these kinds of projects should include increased direct work with the community and increased structured reflection (except in the case of the Peru projects, where there already exists extensive direct cross-cultural interaction and considerable student-faculty reflection and planning).

Finally, the variety of service formats represented above raises an important question: Should service-learning projects be mandatory or elective? In the service-learning literature, opinions on this topic vary. Eyler and Giles (1999) favor required service-learning, basing their position on observed positive cognitive and affective outcomes; i.e., based on the evidence that service-learning is good for students. Clary, Snyder, and Stukas (1998) and Werner (1998), on the other hand, argue for elective service-learning, basing their position on research showing that a required activity reduces intrinsic motivation. In my own questionnaires, 19 percent of 67 ME undergraduates disagreed with the statement "service and academic coursework should be integrated." Eyler and Giles (1999) report a similar percentage in their sample of 1,500 students from across the disciplines. Most of the service-learning projects I described above were required. However, in the future I plan to experiment with more of a mixture of required and elective projects.

Service-learning component	Percentage of course/grade	Hours per student	Assessment
Solar Engineering (22.527)			
Miniprojects: insulation, window analysis; house thermal design	10% (voluntary the first time; required the second time)	20	Report
Capstone Design (22.424)			
Detailed house design	100% (voluntarily choose project)	250	Presentations, report
Mechanical Engineering Lab I (22.302)			
Measure river water quality parameters	10% (required)	15	Poster presentation, report
Mechanical Engineering Lab II (22.403)			
Design projects for thermal and mechanical tests	30% (must choose one of five projects)	45	Presentation, report
Solar Fundamentals (22.521)			
Mini-project: solar access and net gain	10% (required)	20	Presentation
Manufacturing Systems (22.573)			
Experiments and analysis for reliability	+5% (extra credit assignments, voluntary)	10	Report
Design of Energy Systems (24.504)			
Design of solar hot water and crop drying systems	100% (voluntarily choose project)	180	Presentations, report

As the table indicates, assessments of academic content were made through reports and presentations. The quality of the exhibited technical work in general met or exceeded that of previous nonservice-oriented projects and assignments, based on my 15 years of observing and grading student work and based on the capabilities of the students involved.

Student Questionnaire

A questionnaire was devised to obtain basic information from students and to identify their attitudes toward service. It includes 10 statements for which students were asked to rank their responses anonymously, using a five-element, forced-choice scale from -2 (strongly disagree) to +2 (strongly agree). The 10 statements (some of which were adapted from the Colorado Student Service-Learning Questionnaire) read as follows:

1. *The problems of unemployment and poverty are largely the fault of society rather than of individuals.*
2. *Individuals have a responsibility to help solve social problems.*
3. *I don't worry about what's going on in the world because I can't do anything about it.*
4. *It is important to help others even if you don't get paid for helping.*
5. *Engineers should consider the needs of their customers.*
6. *Engineers should put loyalty to their employer ahead of public safety.*
7. *Maybe some people don't get treated fairly, but that is not my concern.*
8. *I can make a contribution to solving some of the problems our nation faces today.*
9. *Engineers can help solve social problems.*
10. *Service and academic coursework should be integrated.*

The responses of students at the beginning of the ME Lab I class in the spring of 1998 are summarized in column one in the table that follows. The responses of those students who completed the second lab course either in the summer of 1998 or in the fall of 1998 are given in the middle column. There is no significant difference in the mean of the responses before and after the service-learning design projects (based on t-tests at the 95 percent confidence level). It is perhaps unrealistic to expect that basic attitudes toward the causes of and solutions to societal problems would change after one relatively small project. Indeed, we could probably infer from these results that several courses with service-learning projects are needed to bring about significant, consistent changes in attitude.

To be sure, Eyler and Giles (1999) do report significant differences in results to similar questions before and after only one semester of service-learning, but the courses they studied seem to have involved more extensive community interaction for essentially the whole length of the course. Other issues make direct comparison of my results with theirs difficult: They used a hierarchical regression analysis, the details of which are unreported; they treated a nonlinear response scale as if it were linear in their analysis; some engineering students were involved with their survey, but the authors give no report as to how many and no separate tally of those responses. Nevertheless,

Average Responses to Statements in Questionnaire
(Date Questionnaire Administered in Parentheses)

	Average Response Before Lab I (Feb 1998)	Average Response After Lab II (July 1998) (Dec 1998)	Average Response After Lab I (May 1999)
Questionnaire Statements:			
Question 1	– 0.04	– 0.51	– 0.07
Question 2	1.43	1.27	0.87
Question 3	– 0.96	– 1.03	– 0.57
Question 4	1.46	1.43	1.23
Question 5	1.79	1.84	1.67
Question 6	– 1.15	– 1.05	– 1.40
Question 7	– 0.75	– 0.58	– 0.87
Question 8	1.04	0.65	0.90
Question 9	1.29	0.95	0.87
Question 10	0.68	0.27	0.83
Student Demographics:			
Number responding	28	37	30
Hours worked weekly	16.1		19.7
Age	25.8		25
Volunteer hours last six months	17.9		27.2
Credit hours currently	14.6		14.1

among the several recommendations Eyler and Giles make is one calling for service-learning students to continue in their work longer than one semester.

In the third column of this table are shown the average responses of the 1999 ME Lab I class after the single experiment involving river monitoring. These responses do not differ significantly from the responses of ME Lab II students, and only on Question 2 is there a significant difference compared with the 1998 ME Lab I group. The students in the ME Lab I group were also asked whether each had spent *much more, more, the same, less,* or *much less time* working on the service experiment than on a nonservice experiment. Fifty-six (56) percent spent the same time, 35 percent spent more time, and the rest (two students) spent less time. Given the due date at the end of the semester, the results seem to indicate the willingness of a significant fraction of the students to work harder on service projects.

It is also important to note that one of the reasons for the lack of significant differences in the responses is the high variability among students responding. For example, the top graph opposite illustrates the tally of responses to Question 10, showing differing degrees of agreement with the idea of integrating service and coursework. In this tally, both 1998 ME Lab II groups and the 1999 ME Lab I group are lumped together. At least 87 percent of the students do not disagree with the notion of combining service with academic coursework.

In a similar manner, the responses to Question 1 indicate a real spread of opinions about the underlying cause of poverty in society: the individual or "the system" (bottom graph). There is a potential for changes in opinions on the part of at least some of the students.

Questionnaires were not given to the students in the more intensive service-learning projects in the design courses because of the relatively low numbers of students.

Observations

The following observations concern the linking of service and coursework as part of an attempt to promote student and community learning about the potential of engineering to help meet community needs:

• It is a challenge to integrate both the subject-matter objectives and the service objectives in a way that does not compromise course objectives.

• This challenge also represents an opportunity for instructors, students, and the community to be creative.

• On the whole, there appears to be diverse (but for the most part positive) student opinions as to whether service-related learning should be integrated into courses.

• The approaches used in this study are adaptable to other school types

Service and academic coursework should be integrated.

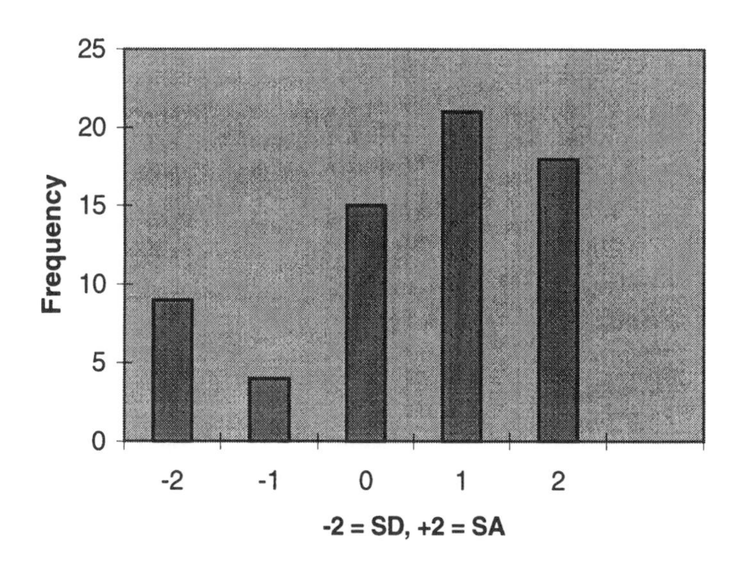

The problems of unemployment and poverty are largely the fault of society rather than of individuals.

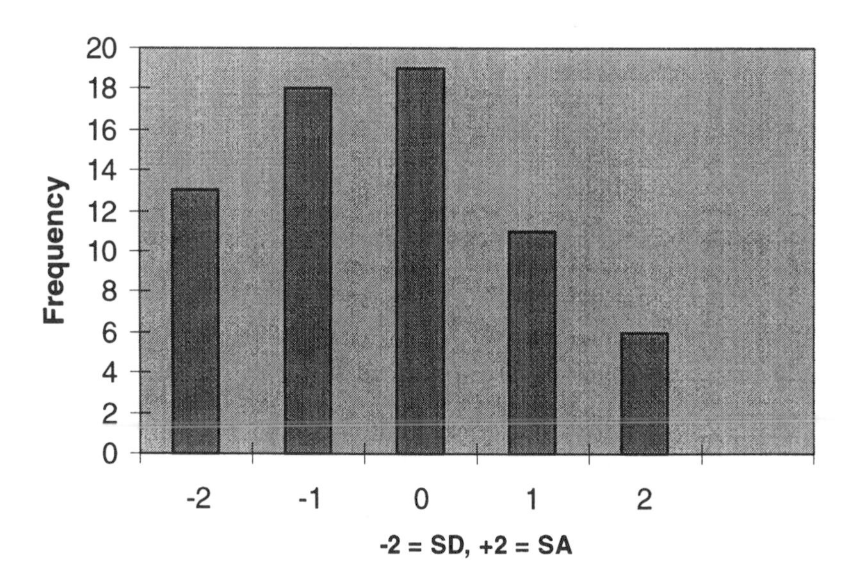

and levels, to other subject matter, and to other communities and geographical regions.

• Changes in student attitude will probably require more intensive service-learning experiences with more direct interaction with the community.

• The above-described service-learning components appear to represent a good start for the process of integrating service and coursework. However, it also appears that more reflection, more direct community interaction and reciprocity (or at least indirect contact, in the case of the international projects), and more formative assessment are needed to reach the goals of the course objectives and the objectives of the entire engineering curriculum, particularly the ABET 2000 objectives.

• The ABET 2000 accreditation guidelines call for traditionally nontechnical objectives (such as those touching on sociology, psychology, and economics), but they also allow for greater flexibility in attaining those objectives. Service-learning appears to be a viable means of integrating those nontechnical areas into engineering courses to meet the ABET objectives.

• Since it appears that a large number of faculty who have become interested in service-learning are well into their careers, service-learning could represent a way for experienced faculty to remain creative and excited about the profession.

In general, the community groups I have worked with (especially Habitat for Humanity and the Peruvian communities) report that they value the students' contributions and are themselves interested in learning more about energy efficiency and solar energy. At the same time, the students are discovering that the concepts they have learned in class can be applied in concrete ways to improve the lives of people in their community, both local and global. They are learning from the community how to make engineering designs, measurements, and analyses more practical, affordable, and consistent with the needs of their "customers."

References

Accreditation Board for Engineering and Technology. (1998). *Engineering Criteria 2000.* Available at the ABET website at <http://www.abet.org/eac/EAC_99-00_Criteria.htm>.

Astin, A., L. Sax, and J. Avalos. (1998). "Long-Term Effects of Volunteerism During the Undergraduate Years." *Review of Higher Education* 22(2): 187-202.

Barr, R., and J. Tagg (November 1995). "From Teaching to Learning: A New Paradigm for Undergraduate Education." *Change* 27(6): 12-25.

Brandenberger, J.W. (1998). "Developmental Psychology and Service-Learning: A Theoretical Framework." In *With Service In Mind: Concepts and Models for Service-Learning in Psychology*, edited by R. Bringle and D. Duffy, pp. 68-84. Washington, DC: American Association for Higher Education.

Clary, E.G., M. Snyder, and A. Stukas. (1998). "Service-Learning and Psychology: Lessons From the Psychology of Volunteers' Motivations." In *With Service In Mind: Concepts and Models for Service-Learning in Psychology*, edited by R. Bringle and D. Duffy, pp. 35-50. Washington, DC: American Association for Higher Education.

Duffy, D., J.J. Duffy, and J. Jones. (1997). "Tuning Up Your Class for Better Mileage: Assessment Tools for Optimal Student Performance." *Journal on Excellence in College Teaching* 8(2): 3-20.

Duffy, J.J. (1998). "Using Service-Learning to Promote Solar Learning." In *National Passive Solar Conference Proceedings*, pp. 443-447. Boulder, CO: American Solar Energy Society.

———, P. Soper, S. Prasitpianchai, D. Villanueva, L. Alegria, and A. Rux. (1999). "PV Systems for Remote Villages: Service-Learning and Communal Sharing." In *Proceedings of the 1999 National Solar Energy Conference*, pp. 27-32. Boulder, CO: American Solar Energy Society.

Eyler, J., and D. Giles. (1999). *Where's the Learning in Service-Learning?* San Francisco, CA: Jossey-Bass.

Hande, H., J. Martin, and J.J. Duffy. (1998). "A Model for Sustainable Rural Solar Electrification in India," In *ASES Conference Proceedings*, pp. 251-258. Boulder, CO: American Solar Energy Society.

Habitat for Humanity. (1998). "Facts About Habitat for Humanity." Website: <http://www.habitat.org>

Honnet, E.P., and S. Poulsen, eds. (1989). "Principles of Good Practice in Combining Service and Learning." A Wingspread Special Report. Racine, WI: The Johnson Foundation.

Jacoby, B., and Associates, eds. (1996). *Service-Learning in Higher Education: Concepts and Practices.* San Francisco, CA: Jossey-Bass.

Werner, C. (1998). "Strategies for Service-Learning: Internalization and Empowerment." In *With Service In Mind: Concepts and Models for Service-Learning in Psychology*, edited by R. Bringle and D. Duffy, pp. 119-127. Washington, DC: American Association for Higher Education.

Acknowledgments

I wish to acknowledge and thank: Donna Duffy for introducing me to concepts of and research on service-learning; the Community Outreach Partnership Collaborative at the University of Massachusetts-Lowell for providing course-release time for some of this work; Ned McCaffrey, a retired engineer and volunteer with the Building Committee of Habitat for Humanity of Greater Lowell; Father Paul Soper, of the UML Catholic Center; and the Office of Community Service at UML for initial contact with Habitat for Humanity.

22.527 Solar Systems Engineering

Miniproject, Spring 1998
Passive Solar Design and Cost/Benefit Analysis for Habitat for Humanity

The local Lowell Habitat for Humanity Chapter is planning to build five new houses on Charles St. (on the south side just about in the middle of the street between Lawrence and Church) with total floor areas of between 1050 and 1200 sq. ft. In order to minimize occupant utility bills, increase comfort levels, and minimize environmental impact, we want to design an energy-efficient house.

Objectives of the thermal design are:

- To reduce the space heating energy use relative to a typical house
- To keep the interior temperatures in a comfortable range
- To minimize the life-cycle costs of the energy system

The scope/deliverables of your design should include:

- Specification of :
  - windows (location, type, and number of glazings)
  - passive solar type(s) and any feature of the solar system
  - insulation levels in walls, ceiling, floor
- Estimation of the heating season energy savings relative to a "standard house"
- Estimation of the interior temperature variations over a typical clear winter day
- Analysis of the 20-year life-cycle solar savings of your house compared to a "standard house" with resale netting 100% of the original price
- Sketches of all four sides of the exterior of the house and any floor plans necessary to convey passive solar system components.

The following assumptions may be made:

- The mortgage interest is zero. The discount rate may be estimated at 4%.
- A "standard house" has R12 walls, R20 ceilings and floors, 8% of the floor area in glazing, and the least expensive double-pane windows.
- The types and costs of building materials are those available at Home Depot. I am not necessarily endorsing Home Depot but simply using its merchandise and costs for comparison purposes. Home Depot does donate building materials to Habitat, however. Consider "green" materials where possible.
- The Habitat house will be roughly 24 X 26 ft with a basement (part slab possible). The long side of the house will face south with the front door on the east side. Natural gas is available for a 90% efficient furnace both the Habitat and "standard" house.

You are expected to spend approximately 20 hours on this project. The final report will be due March 26 and should include the above deliverables along with conclusions. You may work in teams and share material/cost information. You should do your own analysis, however.

Design of a Measurement System and Analysis of Results

ME Lab II, 22.403, Summer/Fall 1998

The purpose of this "experiment" is (a) to design a measurement system and experimental protocol that can be used to evaluate one of the mechanical engineering systems described below and (b) to carry out the protocol and analyze the results. The instrumentation and protocol selected must meet the requirements outlined.

The systems will be used to help build energy efficient, low cost, low maintenance homes in conjunction with the Habitat for Humanity Lowell Chapter and U Mass Lowell Student Chapter. In particular, design the systems to be used on the house currently being rebuilt on Summer St. Actually carry out the experiment on the house or materials from the house.

Select from one of the five projects described below.

A. Ultimate compression yield strength of existing and new wood. The existing "2 X 4" wood support members are roughly 100 years old. You need to check whether they are still have the compressive and bending strength to support the house. Compare the old lumber to new lumber with the same cross section. Repeat for bending. Follow the ASTM standard as closely as practicable.

> Please design the following: (1) a measurement and analysis system to estimate the yield points under compression and bending (three point test) with our equipment in the lab, (2) a method to estimate the uncertainty in these outputs, and (3) a protocol (or procedure) to use in testing the significance of the differences in yield points in the old vs new wood in compression and bending.

B. Calibration of a blower door. A blower door is useful in estimating the leakiness in a building. The blower door in the M.E. Lab needs to have its calibration checked. Design a system to recalibrate the door so that you can predict the air flow into a building as a function of the pressure drop across the fan. Measurements of the pressure drops across the fan can then be made of a building at various static pressure differences between the inside and the outside of the building (P). The flow from your calibration curve can then be used to form a regression equation $V = C\,P^n$ so that flow can estimated as a function of P. The blower door instructions will provide more background information. There is also an ASTM standard that should be studied.

> Please design the following: (1) a measurement and analysis system to calibrate the door under two flow hole configurations, (2) a method to estimate the uncertainty in these outputs (flow) as a function of "flow pressure," and (3) a protocol (or procedure) to use in testing the significance of the differences in flows under the two configurations.

C. Tracer gas test. The actual infiltration over a period of a couple of hours in a building can be estimated with an inert tracer gas (SF_6) and measurements of the gas concentration over time with a gas chromatograph. Infiltration is an important issue in terms of occupant comfort (drafts), occupant health(too little fresh air), and building efficiency (heat loss). There is an ASTM standard regarding such a test. A gas chromatograph is available (courtesy of the Work Environment Department), but its calibration needs to be checked.

> Please design the following: (1) a measurement and analysis system to calibrate the chromatograph, (2) a method to estimate the uncertainty in the infiltration predictions as a function of a time series of tracer

gas concentration measurements and (3) a protocol (or procedure) to use in testing the significance of the differences in infiltration in the Habitat house under two different weather conditions.

D. Daylighting test. Daylight not only saves energy (relative to artificial light) but also has a high quality (resulting in less eye strain and improved vision). A measurement system is needed to see if there is sufficient daylight from the windows in the house at key locations (such as, at kitchen counters, living room reading locations, stairwells). A light meter to measure the luminous intensity (footcandles) is available.

Please design the following: (1) a measurement and analysis system to estimate the luminous intensity at at least three locations on a sunny day and on a cloudy day, (2) a method to estimate the uncertainty in these outputs, and (3) a protocol (or procedure) to use in testing the significance of the differences between light levels and recommended minimum light levels for various tasks.

E. Coheat system for estimating the UA of a small building. (Fall) Electric heaters are used to keep the inside of a small building or house at a constant temperature until the system reaches steady-state. A system must be designed to measure the inside and outside temperatures along with the energy output of the electric heaters so that an estimate of the UA (heat loss coefficient) can be obtained. Assume you have made a rough initial estimate that the UA is 400 Btu/h-F and that the coheat test will be performed in November.

Please design the following: (1) a measurement and analysis system to estimate the heat loss coefficient, (2) a method to estimate the uncertainty in the heat loss coefficient, and (3) a protocol (or procedure) to use in testing the significance of the effect of two wind directions on the heat loss coefficient (due to infiltration). Include the number and location of sensors and heaters and rated output of heaters.

For all the above systems, due to the number of measurements that must be made concurrently, all data must be collected with a PC-based data acquisition system. You may use Labview or Measure software along with one of the DAC PC boards available in the lab.

Presentation and Report

Present the results of your experimental design to the instructors and to the rest of the students on Tuesday, June 23 during the regular lab time. Split the work and presentation with your lab partners. Be sure to include in your presentation the following items from the report outline below: 1,2,3,4,5, and 8.

A final formal lab report from each of the four teams is due July 2. The report should include the design work you have done in addition to actual measurements and analysis carried out. Follow the general instructions in the handout from the writing improvement program.

-2-

Split the work and writing with your lab partners.

Be sure to include as a minimum the following in your report:

1. An outline.

2. The objectives of your design, protocol, and analysis.

3. A description of all sensors chosen, signal conditioning equipment, and data acquisition system (including for each: your selection criteria, supplier, approximate cost, suggested range of operation, and individual uncertainty estimates).

4. The estimated overall uncertainty of the output of your system, based on the manufacturers' sensor/DAS accuracies as well as your own estimates of uncertainties involved with the measurements (e.g., spatial variation effects). Equations and numerical results.

5. The experimental runs needed to test significance of the effects (including the order of the runs). The null hypothesis. The statistical test(s) and criterion(ia) for deciding to reject the null hypothesis (including steps and equations).

6. Data

7. Results

8. Conclusions (e.g.: Did you meet the objectives? Any desirable features of your system?)

Manufacturing Systems 22.573

Extra Credit Miniprojects, November 1998

At the request of a number of those in the class, extra credit is being made available. One or more of the following tasks may be completed and handed in for the number of points indicated. These points are out of 100 for the final grade.

Background: A number of graduate students here are designing and installing photovoltaic systems in remote villages. A group of us is planning to go to the small town of Malvas in Peru in January to modify a PV system in a medical clinic installed last August. The following information would be useful to aid in the design modifications of this system.

1. We are using portable lanterns (Coleman camping lantern with fluorescent bulbs 12 V with a Panasonic 4 amp-hour 12 V sealed lead-acid battery inside). The on-off switches on these lanterns appear to be very unreliable. Perform life testing on three lanterns. From our experience, it should not take too long to get failures. Estimate the 95% confidence interval of the true mean time to failure in cycles. Test to see if a constant failure rate assumption is reasonable. If you are interested, please let me know; we will provide the lanterns. [+2]

2. For a vaccine refrigerator system, we installed 12 PV modules, a battery charge controller, four 105-amp-hour lead-acid deep discharge batteries, and one refrigerator (with solid-state cooling device, Igloo cooler designed to run on a 12 V auto/RV electrical system). Everything operates at a nominal 12 V. Estimate the overall system failure rate (assume constant) (a) with a system failure occurring with the failure of any one component and (b) with a system failure occurring with the failure of any one failure of the following: all the PV modules, all the batteries, the controller, or the refrigerator. You will have to estimate the individual component failure rates from values given in the literature. You can assume that the state of charge of the batteries averages about 60% for failure rate estimation. [+2]

3. It may be possible to model the state of charge of the batteries (i.e., the amount of energy in storage) in the above system as a stochastic process. Assume that the average daily energy delivered from the PV modules is 1125 Wh and that the average daily load of the refrigerator is 575 Wh. You may assume that the delivered energy and the load behave as Poisson processes. Assume that there is a 20% loss of energy in the batteries and that the energy capacity of the batteries is 5000 Wh. The expected MTTF of a battery goes down significantly if the battery state of charge goes below 20% of its rated capacity. Consequently, it is useful to know the estimated long-term proportion of the number of days or cycles that the energy in the batteries falls below 20% of maximum (i.e., below 1000 Wh). Estimate that fraction of time based on your model. Hint: A queuing model might work. [+3]

Any other suitable miniproject involving a topic or topics covered in the course, of your own choosing. Please see me for approval.

ME Lab I 22.302

Uncertainty Experiment: Field Measurements

April 1999

The scope of this experiment includes field measurements of several parameters of a flowing stream in Lowell, analysis of the data, creation of a poster transmitting the results to community organizations, and estimation of the uncertainty in the final results. The goals are to respond to the requests of several community groups (made through several AmeriCorps workers on campus) for information on, and cleanup of, the River Meadow Brook in Lowell and to learn about field measurements, uncertainty in measurements, and communication of results. The objectives are that at the conclusion of this experiment the student will be able to:

- take typical field measurements with portable equipment
- estimate the flow-weighted average of water quality parameters, such as pH, DO (oxygen demand), and temperature
- communicate the results of such measurements to community groups
- estimate the quantitative uncertainty of parameters based on a number of typical lab or field measurements

The River Meadow Brook traverses much of Lowell along the Connector south of the city center. See the attached map. A good sampling location seems to be the small bridge at the south end of Whipple St. Be sure to sample upstream of the point where another small branch of the Concord River cuts into the brook. The brook at this point was roughly 8 feet across on April 5, 1999 and looked to be approximately 3 feet deep in the center. The bridge surface appears to be roughly five feet above the water surface.

We would like to sample several water quality parameters. In each of the four sections, Group One will estimate the stream flow rate (in cubic meters per second and gallons per minute). Group Two will estimate the water temperature (C and F). Group Three will estimate the water acidity (pH). Group Four will estimate the DO (dissolved oxygen, mg/l). At least ten samples or measurements of each parameter at different locations in the cross section of the stream should be taken. The cross section should be weighted by flow rate to the degree possible so that each measurement will be used with equal weighting for the overall average. The ideal would be to take the flow measurements first and then determine approximately locations of the other samples based on those measurements.

In the "lecture" part of the class we will discuss the principle of operation of the sensors you will use and some background of the significance of the use of pH and DO as indicators of water quality. You will be given limits of pH and DO accepted as reasonable for the presence of fish and other biota in freshwater bodies.

A suggested procedure is the following:

1. During your usual lab time (e.g., Tuesday 9:30 am) each group obtain the appropriate sensor(s), DMM, tape measure, plumb bob, and extension stick from the ME Lab. Obtain the calibration coefficients of the sensors. Drive to the sample site. See the attached map. If you need a ride, let the instructor know.

2. BE CAREFUL: PLEASE DO NOT FALL INTO THE BROOK. Try to minimize skin contact with the stream water. I saw a fish swimming in the brook, so the water couldn't be that bad; but be cautious.

3. Use the extension stick, plumb bob, and tape measure to plot a cross section of the stream at the point where you will sample.

4. Take the pitot tube readings (or whatever measurements you think appropriate) to estimate the volumetric flow rate of the stream.

5. Take the readings of temperature, acidity, and DO at the appropriate locations in the stream to obtain a flow-weighted average.

6. Each group prepare a poster by 8:30 am April 22 of the results of your estimate of the average flow, temperature, pH, and DO, respectively. Limit your poster to the equivalent of six sheets of paper 8.5 by 11 inches with font size 24 minimum for text. Include brief descriptions of the purpose, procedure, and results of your measurements and estimate of average water quality parameter. Make some conclusion about the water quality of the brook. In class on April 22 we will vote on the best posters to display at the Earth Day exhibit on campus, which community agencies and neighborhood groups will attend from noon to 6.

7. Estimate the overall uncertainty in your estimate of the flow-weighted average water quality parameter. Include at least three sources of uncertainty in your analysis. Compare your answer to the uncertainty based on the pooled results of all four sections of the lab class. Follow the steps on p. 175-176 in the text:
   A. Define the measurement process.
   B. List all of the elemental error sources.
   C. Estimate the elemental errors.
   D. Calculate the bias and precision error for each measured variable.
   E. Propagate the bias limits and precision indices all the way to the result (average water quality parameter).
   F. Calculate the overall uncertainty of the result.
   Add a seventh step:
   G. Suggest at least one way to reduce the overall uncertainty.

In your report, include the methods (including equations) you used to complete each step and the results at each step. Each lab partner should write a separate report; however, you are encouraged to collaborate with your partner(s) on the analysis. Include your partner's name in your report and acknowledge any cooperative work. The reports are to be turned in to me (John Duffy) by 8:30 am class time on May 11.

ACKNOWLEDGEMENT: Kerry, Glenda, and Dan of AmeriCorps, and MASSPIRG.

-2-

Integrating Service-Learning Into Computer Science Through a Social Impact Analysis

by C. Dianne Martin

> *Computer science should not drive a wedge between the social and the technical, but rather link both through the formal and informal curriculum.*
>
> — Friedman and Kahn 1994

Computer science as an academic discipline continues to advance rapidly, and this advance has caused frequent revision of its curriculum. Since the first formal computer science curriculum was defined in 1968, two major revisions to that curriculum have occurred, the most recent being "Computing Curricula 1991" (ACM/IEEE 1991). An important idea that has emerged in the revisions of the last decade is that the social context and impact of new technologies need to be taken into account in their design, partly because of the ethical implications of their use, and partly because understanding the consequences of use helps to inform and improve the design. In fact, it was specifically stated in "Computing Curricula 1991" that

> *Undergraduates need to understand the basic cultural, social, legal, and ethical issues inherent in the discipline of computing. They should understand where the discipline has been, where it is, and where it is heading. They should understand their individual roles in this process, as well as appreciate the philosophical questions, technical problems, and aesthetic values that play an important part in the development of the discipline. Students also need to develop the ability to ask serious questions about social impact and to evaluate proposed answers to those questions. Future practitioners must be able to anticipate the impact of a given product. Will that product enhance or degrade the quality of life? What will the impact be upon individuals, groups, and institutions?* (11)

To this end, the National Science Foundation funded the ImpactCS Project to define more clearly the learning objectives and pedagogical strategies needed to incorporate this new emphasis into computer science (Huff and Martin 1995; Martin et al. 1996). The strategies suggested for including ethics and social impact issues in computer science included a dedicated course (Martin and Holz 1992), integration of modules into existing courses (Miller 1988), and the inclusion of ethics and social impact as part of the capstone senior design project (Gotterbarn 1992). Whichever strategy or combination of strategies is chosen by a department, there was agreement among experts that this implementation should provide students with the experience of conducting an analysis of the social and ethical impact of a computer system in a real-world setting (Shneiderman 1990; Shneiderman and Rose 1996). Shneiderman (1990) compared such an analysis to the environmental impact statement now required for most engineering projects. Others likened it to an ethnographic case study similar to that which might be conducted by an anthropologist in a new culture, with the computer being viewed as a cultural artifact (Martin et al. 1996). This type of experience has come to be called a "social impact analysis" (SIA).

At the same time that these changes to the computer science curriculum have been occurring, there has been an increasing emphasis in higher education in general, and in the engineering disciplines in particular (ASEE 1994), on providing more educational experiences that not only are grounded in real-world experience but also provide a community service at the same time. This type of educational experience is service-learning: "Method by which students learn and develop through active participation in thoughtfully organized service activities that meet the needs of a community; is integrated into and enhances the academic curriculum of the students; and is coordinated with community organizations" (Tsang, Martin, and Decker 1997: 1). The remainder of this paper presents a case study of how service-learning can be integrated into the computer science curriculum through careful selection of client sites for the SIA.

Social Impact Analysis

In response to new curriculum guidelines calling for including the social and ethical implications of computer technology in the required curriculum, a Technology and Society course has been developed by the Electrical Engineering and Computer Science Department at the George Washington University, in Washington, DC. The course is required for second- and third-year computer science, electrical engineering, and computer engineering students in the School of Applied Science and Engineering. The course, in accord with the learning objectives proposed by the ImpactCS Project (Martin 1997; Martin et al. 1996), presents topics on ethics and social impact of computer technology. The five fundamental knowledge units proposed for this new requirement, designated "ethical and social impact of computing" (ES), are as follows.

> **ES1: Responsibility of the Computer Professional:** *Personal and professional responsibility is the foundation for discussions of all topics in this subject area. The five areas to be covered under the responsibility of the computer professional are: (1) history of the development and impact of*

computer technology, (2) why be ethical? (3) major ethical models, (4) definition of computing as a profession, and (5) codes of ethics and professional responsibility for computer professionals.

ES2: Basic Elements of Ethical Analysis: *Three basic elements of ethical analysis that students need to learn and be able to use in their decision making are: (1) ethical claims can and should be discussed rationally, (2) ethical choices cannot be avoided, and (3) some easy ethical approaches are questionable.*

ES3: Basis Skills of Ethical Analysis: *Five basic skills of ethical analysis that will help the computer science student to apply ethics in their technical work are: (1) arguing from example, analogy, and counterexample, (2) identifying stakeholders in concrete situations, (3) identifying ethical issues in concrete situations, (4) applying ethical codes to concrete situations, and (5) identifying and evaluating alternative courses of action.*

ES4: Basic Elements of Social Analysis: *Five basic elements of social analysis are: (1) the social context influences the development and use of technology, (2) power relations are central in all social interaction, (3) technology embodies the values of the developers, (4) populations are always diverse, and (5) empirical data are crucial to the design and development processes.*

ES5: Basic Skills of Social Analysis: *Three basic skills of social analysis appropriate for computer professionals are: (1) identifying and interpreting the social context of a particular implementation, (2) identifying assumptions and values embedded in a particular system, and (3) evaluating, by use of empirical data, a particular implementation of a technology.*

These learning objectives are taught by providing students with an opportunity to identify stakeholders and ethical issues in concrete situations. Students come to see that technology does not simply impact society in a one-way causal direction; society also influences the shape and development of technology, with the social or organizational *setting* in which a technology is used influencing the *way* in which it is used. Thus, they become aware that social relationships embody implicit and explicit power dimensions and that those dimensions may shift as a result of a new technology. Another important idea they encounter is that the situations in which a technology is used, the people who use it, and the uses to which it will be put are all more varied and diverse than one might at first expect.

To explore these ideas, students are expected to work in teams of three to four persons to systematically collect and analyze empirical data gathered in a social context. This task — identified as a social impact analysis (SIA) — has proven to be a very effective way to enable students to gain experience in assessing the impact of a particular computer system in a real-world setting with real stakeholders. Assessment of all aspects of the SIA represents 35 percent of the grade students receive for the course. Other assignments include an ethics scenario evaluation (10 percent), a science fiction book report (10 percent), current issue critiques (5 percent), use of professional tools (10 percent), discussion-group participation (10 percent), and a final exam (20 percent).

Adding Service-Learning to the SIA

Prior to Spring 1996, students were sent to administrative offices around the George Washington University campus to conduct their SIAs. However, during the spring of 1996 the course instructor teamed up with a representative from GW's Community Services Office and identified 14 sites at off-campus community service organizations. These sites included agencies that provided after-school day care, services to the homeless, senior citizen centers, an AIDS clinic, several public schools, and public health clinics. Each team was provided with an on-campus AmeriCorps liaison to the off-campus site and the following statement of purpose from my syllabus for CS110:

> *The purpose of this project is to give you the experience of working as a team with a real client to produce an analysis of the operation of a computer system in the real world. The clients you will be working with are all involved in providing social services to the local community. They are often overworked, understaffed, and working with very limited or primitive computer resources. Your job is to answer the following questions:*
> - *How are they using the computer to help provide the service?*
> - *What impact is the computer having in their organization?*
> - *Who is using the computer?*
> - *How is it being used?*
> - *Is it viewed as a positive or negative asset in the organization?*
> - *Are there ways that it could be used more effectively?*
> - *Is the delivery of service being helped by the computer?*
>
> *If the client is using the computer to access a database, you will want to ask how the data is verified for accuracy, how the data is protected for privacy, who can access the data, and how it is being used. You need to be aware that some of the data you see or collect could be confidential, so you must assure the client that your final report will be given only to them and to your professor.*

Students were told that their goals in undertaking the analysis were: (1) determine how the system works, the actual vs. idealized practice; (2) develop a strategy to enable them and their client to think about the social and ethical aspects of computer systems; and (3) provide their client with a document that would be useful in future modifications of the system. In particular, they were urged to provide recommendations to help their clients make their computer systems more reliable, secure, and efficient.

To accomplish these goals, students were encouraged to exercise the skills of a social analyst. These included thoughtfulness and imagination in constructing their data-collection interview questions, in selecting places to observe, in dealing with a variety of stakeholders, and in identifying hidden assumptions regarding the use of the technology. They were urged to give attention to detail in data collection and to thoroughness of analysis. They were also given the caveat that they needed to be very respectful of people who might have fewer technical skills than they did. They should approach the assignment as a service they were carrying out for their clients. Because they would be going off-campus to visit some sites that were in questionable areas in the city, they were required to travel in teams of at least two persons at all times.

After making a preliminary site visit, each team had to organize its research plan to include such data-collection techniques as structured interviews, surveys, observations, and content analysis of historical documents. During the course of the semester each team was required to present a written and oral progress report and then, at the end of the semester, a final oral presentation and written report with findings and recommendations. Teams were required to turn in two copies of their reports, one with a cover letter thanking their clients for participating in the project.

Results of the Service-Learning Experience

When the reports of students from this cohort were compared with those of students in previous years, it became apparent that conducting an SIA at a community service agency provided a much more powerful learning experience. In previous years, students had focused on the technology more than on the people at the sites because most of the on-campus sites were doing fairly traditional office work. In the spring of 1996, the students became much more interested in the human aspects of the sites and much more attuned to the social implications of the technology being used there.

Several teams were quite disturbed when they found that the computer equipment at their sites was made up of obsolete technology that had been dumped there — often without any manuals or with key pieces missing — by local businesses that were upgrading their own technology and saw this as an opportunity for a tax-deductible contribution. One team talked about a site with a closet full of old computers where the staff was feeling very guilty about not using them. When the students looked at the equipment, they were immediately able to make the assessment that it was, in fact, useless and obsolete, thus relieving the staff of a deeply felt concern. Another team investigating an after-school program reported:

> *There is a great deal that can be done at this school. It is obvious that the school needs more than three working computers . . . more computers would mean that the students would not have to go to the main office to use them, thereby risking the possibility of the student database being corrupted. In conclusion . . . we think the teachers in For the Love of Children are trying very hard to do a good job, and it would be much easier and better for them if they had more computers to help them.*

They viewed the lack of computer equipment as an equity and access issue for both the teachers and the children.

A team investigating a senior services center also viewed computer usage as an access and equity issue:

> *Care givers as well as senior citizens are meant to have access to this technology . . . volunteers are currently providing introductory courses to the elderly at computer labs in local schools. In the future, however, IONA plans to have its own computer lab.*

Relatedly, a team doing research at a care center for homeless children came to view computers as a tool for empowering children who were otherwise greatly deprived. It felt strongly that the center's computers, rather than paper files, should be used to keep track of the children and that the children themselves should be given access to the computers to increase their logical thinking and confidence levels.

Most of the teams were able to provide useful advice and even some technical assistance to their sites in the process of doing their analysis. For example, the team investigating a day-care center did research to locate a new software package for only $200 that would meet the center's database needs. This was a significant saving from the $900 the center was trying to raise to pay for such software. Each site received a copy of its team's report with recommendations. Two of the sites used their reports to acquire more funds for new computers from their governing boards. A number of the students became so interested in the community service aspect of their project that they expressed a desire to go back to their sites to work as volunteers to do computer training and install new software.

Overall, the addition of a community service aspect to the SIA assignment has greatly enhanced the learning experience and raised the consciousness of students about many of the social issues previously discussed in class. Topics such as the privacy and security of databases became a real concern at the AIDS clinic. Lack of equal opportunity for poor children was brought home when students saw the obsolete computer equipment the children had in their schools and day-care centers. The importance of good record keeping became apparent at the public health clinics. Most students left the course with a firsthand understanding of the ethical and social implications of computer technology and with a greater sense of responsibility for creating future technologies.

One additional aspect of the SIA service-learning course deserves mention. This was the way GW students came to view the assignment itself. In course evaluations at the end of the semester, the SIA projects compared well with other course assignments (where 0 = no value, 1 = some value, 2 = very valuable):

ethics scenario evaluation	1.67
science fiction book report	1.44
current issue critiques	1.50
use of professional tools	1.67
discussion-group participation	1.63
social impact analysis	1.61

In the comments section of the evaluation, students remarked that they viewed the course and the project as very worthwhile and important for engineering and computer science students. Several mentioned that the assignment made the issues in the course much more relevant.

There were, of course, a few difficulties that arose in conjunction with the community-based projects. Students had a hard time scheduling interview and observation time at two of the sites. In both cases, the staff were simply overwhelmed with the amount of work they had to do and didn't feel they had any extra time to help the students. In another case, the clientele and data being handled at the agency (an AIDS clinic) were so sensitive that the students were only allowed to go to the site before or after working hours. This meant they did not have an opportunity to gain a realistic sense of routine computer usage. Several of the AmeriCorps contacts who were supposed to assist the students in their interaction with sites proved to be very unreliable, leaving the students to fend for themselves. Several of the student teams were not sufficiently organized to set up appointments early in the semester. They then tried to do all of their data collection at the last minute, which resulted in an imposition on the client sites and generated several complaints to the professor.

There is one other caveat for faculty interested in organizing similar projects for engineering or computer science students. Finding client sites for SIA projects can be a time-consuming task. Without the assistance of the GW Community Service Office to help locate the 14-17 community service sites needed for a class of 55-70 students, the task would have been monumental. This type of project is best done with small classes (fewer than 30 students) or in a team-teaching environment.

Conclusion

The SIA projects described in this paper illustrate how a service-learning component can be included in the computer science curriculum through a social impact analysis assignment that is targeted at community service agencies. The service-learning aspect of an SIA project contributed to the learning objectives of the course and the assignment by making that assignment more compelling for the students. They were able to relate the abstract social impact and ethical issues in the course to real-world sites that provided services to disadvantaged people. The students had to devise data-collection strategies that were not obtrusive or overly time-consuming for the sites involved. They had to be sensitive to the dignity and privacy of their clients. In a number of cases they were able to provide on-the-spot expertise to help solve minor technical problems with computer hardware and software and to provide a preliminary diagnosis when problems were more serious.

The students involved in these projects learned to work together in teams and were highly engaged and motivated by their interaction with real people. In most cases, they were enthusiastic about their experience. Similarly, the client agencies were, for the most part, very satisfied with their participation in the collaboration and valued the insights and technical expertise the students provided them with. In the long run, however, perhaps the most important result was that the students came to understand at a deeper level the social responsibility that comes with being a member of the computing profession. As Keith Miller (1988) has so aptly stated:

> *Societal and technical aspects of computing are interdependent. Technical issues are best understood (and most effectively taught) in their social context, and the societal aspects of computing are best understood in the context of the underlying technical detail. Far from detracting from the students' learning of technical information, including societal aspects in the computer science curriculum can enhance students' learning, increase their motivation, and deepen their understanding.* (37)

References

ACM/IEEE-CS Joint Curriculum Task Force. (1991). "Computing Curricula 1991." ACM/IEEE-CS Joint Curriculum Task Force Report. New York, NY: ACM Press.

American Society for Engineering Education. (1994). *Engineering Education for a Changing World.* A joint project report of the Engineering Deans Council and the Corporate Roundtable of the ASEE. Available on the ASEE website at <http://www.asee.org>.

Gotterbarn, D. (1992). "The Capstone Course in Computer Ethics." In *Proceedings of the National Conference on Computing and Values: Teaching Computer Ethics,* pp. 41-49. New Haven, CT: Research Center for Computers and Society, Southern Connecticut State University.

Huff, C., and C.D. Martin. (December 1995). "Consequences of Computing: A Framework for Teaching Ethical Computing. (First Report of the ImpactCS Steering Committee)." *Communications of the ACM* 38(12): 75-84.

Martin, C.D. (1997). "The Case for Integrating Ethical and Social Impact Into the Computer Science Curriculum." Paper presented at ACM's Annual Joint Conference Integrating Technology Into Computer Science Education, Uppsala, Sweden, June 1-5.

——— , and H.J. Holz. (1992). "Non-Apologetic Computer Ethics Education." In *Proceedings of the National Conference on Computing and Values: Teaching Computer Ethics,* pp. 50-66. New Haven, CT: Research Center for Computers and Society, Southern Connecticut State University.

Martin, C.D., C. Huff, D. Gotterbarn, and K. Miller. (December 1996). "Implementing a Tenth Strand in the Computer Science Curriculum (Second Report of the ImpactCS Steering Committee)." *Communications of the ACM* 39(12): 75-84.

Miller, K. (1988). "Computer Ethics in the Curriculum." *Computer Science Education* 1: 37-52.

Shneiderman, B. (October 1990). "Human Values and the Future of Technology: A Declaration of Empowerment." *Computers & Society* 20(3): 1-6.

——— , and A. Rose. (February 1996). "Social Impact Statements: Engaging Public Participation in Information Technology Design." In *Proceedings of the Computers and the Quality of Life Symposium,* pp. 90-96. New York, NY: ACM Press.

Tsang, E., C.D. Martin, and R. Decker. (1997). "Service-Learning as a Strategy for Engineering Education for the 21st Century." In *Proceedings of the 1997 American Society for Engineering Education Annual Conference. Milwaukee, WI, June 23-26, 1997.* CD-Rom.

Service-Learning: A Unique Perspective on Engineering Education

by Marybeth Lima

The purpose of this chapter is to describe the method used for implementing service-learning in a biological engineering course at Louisiana State University, and to discuss the impact of this method on the students' educational experiences. Subsequent sections on instructor suggestions and reflections are included to illustrate some of the important dimensions that service-learning brings to the classroom, and to the engineering discipline.

Methods of Course Implementation

Biology in Engineering (BE 1252) is a two-credit-hour (one hour lecture, three hours laboratory per week), second-semester freshman core course to study the "effect of variability and constraints of biological systems on engineering problem solving and design; engineering units; engineering report writing; oral report presentation; laboratory demonstration of biological engineering analysis." Biological engineering involves the application of engineering principles to plants, animals, people, and the environment. A playground design contains these elements and is thus an excellent model to teach students the fundamentals of biological engineering. The majority of the learning experiences in the course were integrated into the semester-long service-learning project.

The school (Beechwood Elementary, in Baton Rouge, LA) was chosen for the SL project based on the following criteria: (1) The institution had just been named a science and mathematics magnet school, and significant effort was being expended by faculty and administration on generating interest and academic achievement in these areas. This imparted an educational element to the project among all the students. (2) The institution was in dire need of playground equipment. (3) The potential for community building was excellent. Three separate playground areas exist at the school: one for prekindergarten and kindergarten students, one for grades 1 and 2, and one for grades 3 through 5. This diversity allowed each of the 40 students enrolled in BE 1252 to choose to design one of three play areas, which cut down on the number of designs for each area.

SL Project Approach

The success of the project required collaboration and buy-in from the following parties: (1) BE 1252 students and instructor; (2) Beechwood students and teachers; and (3) Beechwood administration. Meetings with teachers and administrators occurred before the project was initiated, to coordinate schedules, lesson plans, and meetings between college and elementary school students. Six Beechwood students from grades K-5 were selected by their teachers to participate, for a total of 30 students. The BE 1252 students were split into groups of three to four members based on their interest in the Beechwood play areas and instructor discretion. These groups were maintained throughout the semester.

Several activities occurred before the BE 1252 students and their Beechwood clients met. College students met with the school principal on an initial field visit to collect background information and geographical data. Beechwood students were encouraged to envision their dream playground in exercises (such as drawing) facilitated by their teachers and the BE 1252 instructor. The BE 1252 students participated in activities and instruction regarding playground design.

In their first meeting, BE 1252 students interviewed the elementary school students to determine the type of equipment they would like to use, and activities in which they would like to participate on their school playground. The drawings of the Beechwood students' dream playgrounds gave all parties a place to begin their discussion. The college students then created playground drawings and specifications (on AutoCAD) according to the suggestions given to them by the K-5 students. These designs were presented to an expert panel consisting of playground designers and inspectors for critical review. The groups of students met a final time so that the K-5 students could provide a critique of the designs and suggest potential changes. Eleven independent playground designs were created as a result of this project: five for the preK/K area, four for the grades 1-2 area, and two for the grades 3-5 area. All BE 1252 students received their first choice of play area to design. (It is interesting to note that almost all the preK/K designers were female, and all the grades 3-5 designers were male.)

BE 1252 Classroom Activities to Complement the SL Project

Classroom activities were given to correspond to steps encountered in the engineering design process. The table opposite describes the assignments and lab exercises conducted during the course.

Overall Course Structure

Each student was required to maintain a student portfolio (Christy and Lima 1998; Lima et al. in press) that included all the assignments in conjunction with the SL project. The portfolio was worth 40 percent of the course grade. The SL project report (including drawings, specifications, and a written report) was worth 10 percent of the grade. An individual grade for

Engineering method	Classroom activities and assignments for SL project	Time during semester
Identification of the problem	introduction to SL project	1
Information gathering	instruction on playground design; library/Internet searches; visit to/critique of existing playgrounds; observation of a playground installation, visits to Beechwood students	1, 2, 3
Search for creative solutions, generation of preliminary designs	creation of individual "dream playgrounds"; brainstorming, creativity exercises	2, 3
Evaluation/selection of final design	discussions with experts, instructor, group members, clients; simple calculations; decision charts; critique by expert panel	3, 4
Preparation of reports, plans, specifications	classroom instruction re: technical writing, preparation of specifications reports	4
Implementation	visits to Beechwood students	4

Note: Numbers 1 - 4 listed in the *time during semester* column indicate the quadrant of the semester in which the activity was performed by the students, with 1 representing the first quarter of the semester (Weeks 1-4) and 4 representing the last quarter of the semester (Weeks 13-16).

the SL project constituted another 10 percent; this was determined through a confidential assessment of each student by the other group members, each student's self-assessment, and the instructor's assessment. The assessment instrument was designed by the students and the instructor, and included criteria such as attendance, effort and attitude, teamwork, communication, and dependability. A midterm and final exam were the remaining components of the grade.

Instruction on working effectively in groups was included because, in the author's experience, students do not work well together unless they are clear on agendas, roles, guidelines, and methods of conflict resolution (Covey 1989; Jalajas and Sutton 1985; Kroeger and Thuesen 1988). A specific unit on creativity (Gelb 1998) was included to increase student motivation and confidence.

The final goal was for the students and interested members of the community to build the three playground areas Habitat for Humanity–style. Consolidation of the initial designs and fundraising are currently under way to achieve this. The fact that the instructor teaches the next consecutive course in the curriculum makes possible year-long contact with the participating students. Clearly, such an expanded time frame supports SL project implementation.

Results

Teachers and administration involved in the SL project believe it was a success from their observations of student motivation and civic responsibility. The author believes that student comments on a self-assessment narrative at the conclusion of the course best sum up the results of using such an SL project.

This kind of project was employed for a number of reasons. First, to enhance the "big picture" involving engineering design. If students are able to experience a tangible purpose and framework for the fundamental courses they take during the first two years of their curriculum, they are more likely to be motivated and understand why they are learning the required material. Student comments that illustrate this point include the following:

> *I also learned that designing something for someone is not as easy as I thought. You have to consider cost, area, stipulations, ADA (Americans With Disabilities) regulations, your clients, time, materials, and dimensions. It's a whole lot to consider.*

> *In working with the Beechwood students, I was able to more fully understand how engineering works, and learning to understand that there are*

more than numbers, figures, and statistics to engineering.

. . . what I learned from all of this is that big and fancy is not always better.

Another major impetus for using an SL project was to help sharpen the students' communication skills. Because employers often report a lack of communication skills (written, oral, and team) in entry-level engineers, the course (and the curriculum) is geared to provide frequent, varied communication experiences. Communicating with children as clients provided an interesting, challenging experience.

I learned that a large part of the success of a design is knowing how to get the best description of what the client desires. We had to be creative in getting the children at Beechwood to express their wants through their drawings, friendly conversation, and observation of which equipment they played on most. It took a great deal of listening and observing to get the overall needs of the clients. . . .

I think the Beechwood project was an excellent idea because I learned a lot from it, not just how to design a playground. While working with the pre-K and kindergarten students, I learned how to alter my way of thinking to conform to the situation at hand. In other words, I discovered that if I was going to design a playground that was appealing to them and communicate my ideas, I had to think like them. I think that this was a giant leap for me as an engineering student.

Finally, an SL project was chosen to give students the opportunity to see beyond themselves and their education into the community at large, and to experience civic responsibility. This project required most students to cross racial and economic boundaries. The response of the students and their written reflections on social issues were encouraging in this regard.

These children have been deprived of what we most take for granted: a place where we can go to escape and play and relax. Although we read in class about Piaget's stages of development and how a playground enhanced a child's growth, it didn't really sink in until I visited the school.

Through working with the Beechwood students I realized that time has not changed the playground equipment that children prefer. . . . Even though I grew up in the suburbs and was raised in a totally different environment than the Beechwood kids, I realized that the kids are just the same as my friends and I were at that age. Play seems to extend beyond all cultural boundaries.

The most striking aspect of my Beechwood experience was the attitudes of the children. They were anxious to get a new playground, but were not feeling deprived by the one they have now. They make the best use of the play equipment they already have.

All students reported a positive experience with working in groups. Classroom instruction on conflict resolution and the fundamentals of working in teams was responsible for this success. Problems in student groups occurred in previous years when instruction on teaming was not offered.

Comments were also gathered from Beechwood Elementary students and administrators at the end of the school year. These demonstrated a positive impact with regard to K-5 student understanding, learning, and motivation. A sampling of the children's comments includes:

- *I liked designing things for the playground. I can't wait to see it when we finish.*

- *I want to make more [playground] models. . . .*

- *Maybe we could go from school to school telling them how to do playgrounds.*

- *That was so fun. We enjoyed talking to the students from LSU. I may go to LSU when I grow up.*

Beechwood administrators were also enthusiastic about the project:

- *This will be our first real project with a university. We've got great plans to make this project part of a social studies unit on communities. Becoming a true community school is our goal.*

- *This is the first time our students have had the chance to work on a project of this kind. They're proud of themselves. I wish we had more of these kinds of activities.*

- *We've seen remarkable interest shown by our students. They're always anxious to get started.*

Interactive, student-centered learning opportunities are valid and available through industry-sponsored projects. But completing a community service project is critical for developing civic awareness and social responsibility, two elements often overlooked in engineering education. Emphasizing the social component of engineering could enhance the attractiveness of the engineering discipline, particularly for women and minorities. Indeed, the retention rate for women and minorities in the three years that SL projects have been implemented in this course has been substantially higher than the national average, as the table at the end of this chapter indicates.

Instructor Suggestions

1. **Get connected.** Service-learning is an underexploited tool, though much more SL is currently occurring in the engineering classroom than has been reported, discussed, and disseminated. Organizations such as Campus Compact serve as broad consortiums for networking and information/publication disbursal regarding SL. Many individual universities have SL programs that cut across all disciplines, though such programs might not specifically contain the term "service-learning." Get connected with others doing SL; having colleagues to collaborate with in this regard is invaluable.

2. **Try to provide a multidisciplinary dimension to the project.** The connection of engineering to other disciplines can be reinforced using SL. For example, one important component of the playground design was a cost analysis. A business course could include an SL component for the playground project by preparing a business plan, while a communications course could develop a public relations plan for the project. These types of activities would reinforce the multidisciplinary, cross-functional teamwork approach true of a real-world job setting. Institution-wide SL programs can serve as facilitators for integrating both instructors and projects across the disciplines. However, become involved in such ventures only after acquiring some personal experience with SL projects, as the logistics of SL add an extra layer of complexity to course planning. The EPICS (Engineering Projects in Community Service) program at Purdue University is a good model in this regard (described elsewhere in this volume).

It is interesting to note that Beechwood Elementary School is itself using a multidisciplinary approach to this project by emphasizing the science and math skills needed for playground building, the development of artistic ability for drawing and modeling playgrounds, and the social studies and community-building dimensions of the overall project.

3. **Take legal ramifications into account.** If a structure or device is built for use in the community, liability issues must be considered. In general, student designs must be certified by a professional engineer before they are implemented. Contact appropriate legal counsel at one's university for guidelines. Consulting with local Habitat for Humanity chapters can yield useful information on how to proceed with student-supported projects at the university-community level.

Reflections

SL resonates with my passionate belief that engineering must truly address social issues and fully interface with society to be a vital, positive influence. From a historical perspective, engineers have promoted the creation of human living spaces and creature comforts and facilitated the Industrial Revolution and the Information Age. However, the narrow focus on technical aspects of problem solving and the accompanying "conquer nature" paradigm have created other problems. The human population explosion and its consequences (endangerment and extinction of countless plant and animal species, environmental pollution, global warming, etc.) are due in large part to technological advances. I define social engineering as solving problems and achieving goals in the context of society while neutrally or positively affecting the planet and its inhabitants. This dimension must be considered in the engineering discipline if we are to avoid the dire consequences of our currently narrow focus. Although some engineering educators are doing excellent work in this area (Atman and Nair 1996; Pantazidou and Nair 1999), SL can add an integral component to this concept by simultaneously teaching students engineering *and* social responsibility, and how their work impacts the community, society, and the world.

References

Atman, C., and I. Nair. (1996). "Engineering in Context: An Empirical Study of Freshmen Students' Conceptual Frameworks." *Journal of Engineering Education* 85(4): 317-326.

Besterfield-Sacre, M., C. Atman, and L. Shuman. (1997). "Characteristics of Freshman Engineering Students: Models for Determining Student Attrition in Engineering." *Journal of Engineering Education* 86(2): 139-149.

Christy, A., and M. Lima. (1998). "Student Portfolios in Engineering Instruction." *Journal of Engineering Education* 87(2): 143-148.

Covey, S. (1989). *The 7 Habits of Highly Effective People*. New York, NY: Simon & Schuster.

Gelb, M. (1998). *How to Think Like Leonardo Da Vinci: Seven Steps to Genius Every Day*. New York, NY: Delacorte Press.

Jalajas, D., and Sutton, R. (1985). "Feuds in Student Groups: Coping With Whiners, Martyrs, and Deadbeats." *The Organizational Behavior Teaching Review* 10: 94-102.

Kroeger, O., and J. Thuesen. (1988). *Type Talk: The 16 Personality Types That Determine How We Live, Love, and Work*. New York, NY: Dell Publishing.

Lima, M., A. Christy, M. Owens, and J. Papritan. (in press). "The Use of Student Portfolios to Enhance Learning and Encourage Industrial Ties in Undergraduate Education." *NACTA Journal*.

Pantazidou, M., and J. Nair. (1999). "Ethic of Care: Guiding Principles for Engineering Teaching and Practice." *Journal of Engineering Education* 88(2): 205-212.

Strenta, C., R. Elliott, M. Matier, J. Scott, and R. Adair. (1993). *Choosing and Leaving Science in Highly Selective Institutions: General Factors and the Questions of Gender.* New York, NY: Alfred P. Sloan Foundation.

———. (1995). *Engineering Education: Designing an Adaptive System.* Washington, DC: National Academy Press.

Acknowledgments

This study was funded by the LSU College of Agriculture, the LSU Division of Instructional Support and Development, and the Louisiana Board of Regents LaCEPT (Louisiana Collaborative for Excellence in the Preparation of Teachers) program. The author would like to thank Beechwood Elementary employees Georgia Jenkins (principal), Laura East (assistant principal), Mary Price (counselor), and Albertha Warren (guidance counselor) for helping to execute the project. Sally Donlon and Sara Carr of LaCEPT assisted with project administration. The following BE 1252 students contributed comments: S. Monique Angelle, Tessa Byrne, Nyx D'Albor, F. David Gatz, Bilal Ghosn, Andrea Leonards, Amy Manabat, and H. Donielle Meades. Beechwood Elementary students Travis Dunn, Carlandria Davis, Todd Hopkins, and Katrina Jackson also contributed comments, in addition to Beechwood administrators Georgia Jenkins, Laura East, and Albertha Warren.

BE 1252 student William Weber died in April 1999. I and his fellow students mourn this loss. His presence in the LSU Department of Biological and Agricultural Engineering will be missed.

	Percentage of class	Class retention rate (%)	National retention rate (%)
Women	37	93	~70 (Strenta et al. 1993)
Minorities	12	93	~70 (Strenta et al. 1995)
All Students	100	82	~ 76 (Besterfield-Sacre et al. 1997)

Note: Class retention rates (%) were calculated for students who remained in engineering between the freshman and sophomore years (n = 110). National retention rate data for women and minorities were estimated using overall retention rate data (Atman and Nadir 1996; Besterfield-Sacre, Atman, and Shuman 1997) and the fact that approximately half of all students are lost between the freshman and sophomore years.

Integrating Service-Learning Into "Introduction to Mechanical Engineering"

by Edmund Tsang

In the fall of 1993, faculty members of the Mechanical Engineering (ME) Department of the University of South Alabama (USA) began a self-study to evaluate the undergraduate curriculum as part of their preparation for the school's next accreditation visit in 1999. At the time, the Accreditation Board for Engineering and Technology (ABET) was moving away from counting the number of design hours to design-across-the-curriculum as a criterion for evaluating engineering programs (ABET 1992). The self-study team was aware of calls for curricular reform by organizations such as the American Society for Engineering Education (ASEE 1994) and the National Science Foundation. The Green Report, published jointly by the Engineering Deans Council and the Corporate Roundtable of ASEE in October 1994, identified many curricular objectives sometimes referred to as "softer skills" (ASEE 1994); e.g., communication skills, teamwork, appreciation of diversity, and awareness of the social aspects of engineering. Under ABET's *Engineering Criteria 2000* (ABET 1998), engineering programs will, in fact, be required to document student performance in these softer skills.

In the course of its curricular review, the ME faculty identified two weaknesses in the first two years of the curriculum. First, students received little instruction and practice in engineering design in their lower-division courses. Second, the one-credit Introduction to Mechanical Engineering, meeting for 50 minutes nine to 10 times per academic quarter, was unsatisfactory and not, in fact, very effective as an introduction to engineering.

As a result of the review, a new curriculum was put in place beginning in the fall of 1995 that introduced into the first two years three new courses with substantial design content. A four-credit-hour Introduction to Mechanical Engineering, ME 125, was one of the new courses introduced. This course has many of the features of model Introduction to Engineering courses as described in recent ASEE publications — except that service-learning provides the context for students to learn and practice technical design while developing some of the softer skills now being called for (Gerbec, Skillman, and Conrad 1994; Hart, Engerer, and Goodman 1994; Herzog 1994; Kozick 1994).

Identification of a Community Need

Public education in the state of Alabama in general and in Mobile County in particular has never received the full support it needs. Alabama regularly ranks near the bottom among states in per capita spending for public education, and local expenditures put Mobile County among the bottom-five school systems in the state. Furthermore, the majority of mathematics and science teachers in Alabama's middle schools are not certified in these subjects. Low funding for public education in Mobile County means that public school teachers have few opportunities to remedy professional deficiencies.

In Fall 1993, the University of South Alabama Chapter of Sigma Xi sponsored a forum to identify ways in which USA faculty members could contribute to improving mathematics and science instruction in the county's public schools. A panel of teachers, principals, and administrators identified resources needed to support active, hands-on learning. As it turned out, this need for resources to support hands-on learning in mathematics and science complemented the educational purpose of ME 125; namely, that first-year engineering students learn and practice an engineering design process consisting of

(1) formulating a design problem based on identified needs;

(2) generating, analyzing, and selecting solutions based on design constraints and criteria;

(3) communicating and implementing a solution; and

(4) evaluating that solution for continuous improvement.

In carrying out their designs, students would also have an opportunity to practice teamwork and communication skills. The actual design projects for ME 125 would consist of first-year student teams working to design and produce hardware and software needed by the public school teachers.

Course Design

Goals and Objectives

The service-learning projects in Introduction to Mechanical Engineering have two explicit goals:

- ME students will learn and practice the engineering design process.
- ME students will produce hardware and software to support active, hands-on learning of mathematics and science in Mobile County middle schools.

The course designers chose to partner with middle schools because middle school mathematics describes many interesting, everyday examples of engineering. Furthermore, middle school students represent a critical group in the pool of potential future scientists, engineers, and mathematicians, since interest in mathematics and science among elementary school students is high but drops off rapidly in the middle school years. Still another reason for choosing middle schools for partners was that the knowledge base needed for such a project would not impose a burden on first-year ME students, thus allowing them to focus on the creativity and process aspects of their work.

But knowledge of the design process constitutes only the first of ME 125's three key learning objectives:

- *Learning Objective #1 — Students will demonstrate knowledge and practice of the engineering design process.*
- *Learning Objective #2 — Students will demonstrate teamwork.*
- *Learning Objective #3 — Students' self-reported levels of community-civic responsibility will increase.*

Assessment

Each of the objectives just identified demands its own assessment measures. These include:

- *Learning Objective #1 is assessed by a written final project report evaluated by the instructor and a final project oral presentation evaluated by a faculty member other than the instructor.*
- *Learning Objective #2 is assessed through a combination of pre- and postservice surveys, written comments, and minutes kept by the design team.*
- *Learning Objective #3 is assessed through pre- and postservice surveys and written comments.*

The survey questions used to assess the impact of the service-learning projects on students' attitudes toward teamwork and their sense of community-civic responsibility have been developed by Drs. R. Burke Johnson, E. Jean Newman, and Jim Van Haneghan, of USA's Behavior Studies and Education Technology Department, College of Education.[1] Some of the survey questions to assess teamwork are taken from the work of Anwar (1995).

Implementation

Community Partners

As has been noted, the community partners involved in this initiative are middle school teachers from the Mobile County Public School System (MCPSS). In year one (1995-1996), teachers were recruited with the help of the school system's Southeastern Consortium for Minorities in Engineering (SECME) program coordinator. This first year, applicants had to apply in teams consisting of a mathematics or science teacher and a language arts or social studies teacher from the same school. In years two and three (1996-1998), the criterion was changed to a team consisting of a mathematics teacher and a science teacher from the same school. Also, the target pool was expanded to include all MCPSS middle school teachers. The teachers were provided with a small stipend from a grant from the Corporation for National Service for their involvement.[2]

An orientation was held at the beginning of the academic quarter. The teacher-partners received a description of the service-learning project, the project time line, the instructor's expectations in the form of a one-page Q&A information sheet, and a short presentation and discussion led by the course instructor. Faculty expectations for the teacher-partners included their meeting with the student design teams to provide information and feedback; their implementing and evaluating the hardware and software designed and produced; and their participating in a debriefing at the conclusion of the project. The teacher-partners were also surveyed at the orientation as to what they expected of the engineering faculty and the engineering students.

The orientation was followed by a workshop led by a faculty member from the College of Education who specializes in instructional design. Topics covered in the workshop included writing learning objectives and developing lesson plans for math and science, and issues related to mathematics and science education for the 21st century. Teachers also met with engineering faculty to discuss their hardware and software needs with regard to the learning objectives they had identified. To assess the effectiveness of the workshop, the teachers filled out pre- and postworkshop surveys.

Engineering Students

Students studied the engineering design process and best practices of teamwork through case studies in weeks one-three. Teamwork materials were taken from the work of Bellamy et al. (1994). During the third week of the quarter, design teams received a memorandum from the instructor identifying the two teacher-clients assigned to them and a general statement of the teachers' needs. The teams then met with their clients to gather background information. They also visited the teachers' schools to gain a sense of the environment in which the requested designs would be used.

Students were required to submit two individual progress reports on their service-learning projects: the first on problem definition and design project statement; the second on solutions generation, analysis, and selection. Design teams were required to fill out, each time they met among themselves or with their teacher-clients, a meeting log the instructor could use to monitor their progress.

The last two weeks of the course were primarily free periods for students to complete their design projects, to write their final project reports, and to prepare for oral presentations. The design teams were required to demonstrate the hardware and software they had designed and produced for their clients, and to gather client feedback before writing a final report.

To complete the project, each design team presented to the teacher-clients a manual in addition to the hardware produced. The teams were also required to submit a written report to the instructor and make a final oral presentation. To make the service-learning projects more realistic, each design team is given a budget of $50.

Service-Learning Design Projects

Some examples of projects undertaken by students enrolled in ME 125 from 1995 to 1998 include the design and production of

- Pencil rocket launchers and a simple sextant to measure the height of a rocket's flight. They were made for a middle school SECME club.
- A flush-toilet demonstrating the engineering concepts of lever and gravity-feed. Middle school students used the toilet to collect, graph, and analyze data while studying such things as volume, units for volume measurement, the lever law, and the use of simple algebra to build models of engineering phenomena.
- Activities based on the construction of the Pyramid of Giza. Middle school students thus had an opportunity to practice skills in measuring and collecting data, apply the concept of ratio to solve problems, and practice the skills needed to construct a mathematical model.
- A windmill and an anemometer that allowed middle school students to investigate wind speed and wind energy.
- A solar cooker, a model greenhouse, and support for a solar panel to equip an outdoor classroom.
- Equipment and activities needed to support an after-school science club where middle school students could collect data to observe and verify Newton's principles regarding force, motion, and energy.
- Activities and supplies needed to support the teaching of System International units in length and mass.
- A briefing manual to help prepare a pair of middle school teachers who were to be their school's sponsors at a Science Olympiad on bridge building. The manual consisted of a history of bridge building and types of bridges as well as models of various types of trusses.

Results

As was noted above, Introduction to Mechanical Engineering has three objectives that need to be evaluated.

Learning Objective #1

Students will demonstrate knowledge and practice of the engineering design process. This objective is assessed by a written report evaluated by the instructor and an oral presentation evaluated by an engineering faculty member other than the instructor. Evaluation of the oral presentation is based on the following criteria: Overall Design (30 percent); Clarity of Presentation (30 percent); Use of Visual Aids (20 percent); Teamwork (10 percent); and Ability to Answer Questions (10 percent). The scores of individual students for both the written report and the oral presentation are calculated from the team scores by a weighing factor based on peer evaluation of each team member's contribution and effort toward completing the design project.

The involvement of an engineering faculty member other than the course instructor ensures objectivity in the evaluation process. The grade distribution for the 96 students enrolled in Introduction to Mechanical Engineering from 1995 to 1998 is shown in the top table opposite.

As is immediately apparent, the written report evaluations and the oral presentation evaluations provided by the two engineering faculty members were quite similar. Overall, their assessments of 87 of 96 students, or 90.6 percent, were in agreement; 86.4 percent of the students received a grade of B or higher for their written report; and 80.1 percent of them a grade of B or higher for their oral presentation.

Learning Objective #2

Students demonstrate teamwork. The teamwork process is tracked by minutes of meetings kept by the design teams. This allows the instructor to follow the progress of the design projects and the division of labor among team members. Attitudes of students toward teamwork are evaluated by pre- and postsurveys and written comments. The results of pre- and post-service surveys on student attitudes toward teamwork for years one and two of the project are summarized in the bottom table opposite.

When students were asked to identify three skills they developed through the service-learning design project, teamwork was mentioned approximately twice as often as any of 11 other skills. Teamwork skills cited by the students include "cooperative learning," "the ability to communicate with team members," "recognition of roles within the group," "working with

Grade Distribution on Service-Learning Projects

Grade	Written Report (evaluated by instructor)	Oral Presentation (evaluated by another faculty member)
A (90-100%)	51 students (53.1%)	53 students (55.1%)
B (80-89%)	32 students (33.3%)	24 students (25%)
C (70-79%)	6 students (6.3%)	9 students (9.4%)
D (60-69%)	2 students (2.1%)	6 students (6.3%)
F (<60%)	5 students (5.2%)	4 students (4.1%)

Results of Pre- and Post-Service Survey on Teamwork

Academic Quarters	Change Between Pre- and Post-Service Survey
Winter 1996	Negative -- statistically insignificant
Spring 1996	Negative -- statistically insignificant
Winter 1997	Positive -- statistically insignificant
Spring 1997	Positive -- statistically insignificant

others," "sharing ideas and working in a group," "designing a project to suit others," and "importance of total group involvement."

An inconsistency appeared in the results for years one and two between the quantitative assessment (pre- and postservice survey using Likert-type scales) and the qualitative assessment (responses to open-ended questions) of this objective. The inconsistency could be attributed to: (1) students at the beginning of the quarter with little awareness of the issues tending to rate themselves high (ceiling effect), (2) students tending to rate themselves high in socially desirable ways, and (3) small sample size and nonrandom selection (Johnson, Newman, and Van Eck 1997). As a result, the approach to assessing student attitudes toward teamwork was modified in year three to utilize an instrument more qualitative in nature.

In this third year, students filled out a midterm evaluation (week three), after they had been assigned their design project. With regard to teamwork, they were asked to answer the following question:

> *You have recently started your design project involving work with school teachers to design equipment that can be used in math and science education. What tools and skills have you acquired so far that will help you to complete the project? Specify what they are and how they will help you.*

In the postservice survey, the students were asked the same question plus five other questions on teamwork. These questions are:

> *1. You have recently completed your design project involving work with school teachers to design equipment that can be used in math and science education. What tools and skills did you acquire in the ME 125 (Introduction to Mechanical Engineering) course that helped you to complete the project? Specify what they were and how they helped you.*
>
> *2. Team and Group Processes (Answer the questions below on a separate sheet. Please explain your answers.)*
>
> *a) You did your project as a team:*
>
> *(i) What was the best part of working on the project as a team?*
>
> *(ii) What was the worst part of working as a team?*
>
> *b) How did your team get along?*
>
> *c) Did people carry out their assignments?*
>
> *d) How relevant is doing work in teams to engineering?*
>
> *e) If you had a choice, would you rather do the project working with a team or by yourself?*

In the midterm survey, only 10 of 13 students enrolled in ME 125 returned the preservice survey, giving a response ratio of 0.77. There was a range of responses to the question about the skills and tools students thought would help them with the project, and only one student mentioned teamwork. In the postsurvey, all 13 students participated; two students mentioned teamwork in response to that same question.

The following responses were recorded for the five postservice survey questions concerning team and group processes.

a) Best and Worst Parts of Team Experience: Regarding the positive aspects of working in groups, three students mentioned a reduction in workload as something positive. Three students mentioned that the solution the group arrived at was better than what they could have accomplished alone; and two students mentioned having the help of others as a positive element. Two mentioned the importance of learning about alternative perspectives on a problem; one student mentioned meeting new people; and one student mentioned the group's working well together.

Negative aspects of working in a team were less varied. Six students mentioned that scheduling was problematic; three students mentioned arguing and dissension as a problem. One mentioned that he or she did not like depending on others; one student mentioned the absence of a team member at meetings as a negative; and one student offered nothing negative.

b) How Well Did the Group Get Along? All 13 students responded that the members of their teams got along well.

c) Did Team Members Carry Out Their Assignments? All students indicated that their team members carried out their assignments.

d) How Relevant Is Teamwork to Engineering? Twelve students stated teamwork was very relevant, with one of them going so far as to suggest that teaming skills were one of the most important skills that an engineer could possess. One student did not respond to this question.

e) Do You Prefer to Work in Teams or Alone? Twelve students indicated they would rather work in groups, with one student stating he or she would work in a group if he or she could choose the group members. One student indicated that he or she would rather work alone.

Generally, working in a team was viewed as positive, and many advantages were cited such as time savings, exposure to multiple viewpoints, and better solutions. Only two students seemed to have some reservations about working in groups: One wanted to pick his or her team members, and the other mentioned that he or she did not like feeling dependent on others for his or her grade. However, picking one's team members or working alone is not an option in the working world, where engineers must work with clients and others whom they may like or dislike.

Learning Objective #3

Students' self-reported levels of community-civic responsibility will increase. The changes in student attitude on community-civic responsibility were measured by pre- and postservice surveys and written comments in years one and two. The table that follows summarizes the results of pre- and postservice survey changes in student attitudes during this period.

The results of this quantitative assessment suffer from the same weaknesses described above with regard to student attitudes toward teamwork. In the open-ended responses of the postservice survey, students listed "benefiting society" as a definition of engineering, along with "problem solving" and "design." "Benefiting society" was either the most or the second most important benefit, according to student responses.

It should be noted that one student in winter 1996 objected to the community service aspect of the design projects and organized a complaint to the department chair. Despite this student's complaint, which might have influenced the opinions of other students, the majority of student comments regarding their service-learning projects and the course were very positive. For example, 14 out of 18 students in winter quarter 1997 submitted written comments. Of the 14 comments, there were 10 positive comments about the course; three complaints about the team selection process (although two of these complaints included positive comments about the course in general); and one negative comment about the amount of writing involved. For spring quarter 1997, 15 of 18 students provided comments. There were 12 positive comments about the course, one suggestion ("change the project to high school students so we could delve deeper into more complex math concepts"), and two negative comments ("the number and timing of the project" and "the amount of writing in the course"). Some examples of positive written comments include:

> *I had a great time! The hardest work you will ever love.*

> *Keep trying hard to do something productive for the community.*

> *Excellent class that prepares ME students for the real world.*

> *I learned a lot from this class, like organization, communication, and how to get on your feet.*

> *I really was impressed with the complexity of this freshman-level course. Students are introduced to the design process, required to write reports, and communication is emphasized. Without those items, engineering will not take place.*

Results of Pre- and Post-Service Surveys of Student Attitudes Toward Community-Civic Responsibility

Academic Quarters	Change Between Pre- and Post-Service Surveys
Winter 1996	Negative -- statistically significant
Spring 1996	Positive -- statistically significant
Winter 1997	Positive -- statistically significant
Spring 1997	Positive -- statistically insignificant

Most enjoyable class at USA.

I enjoyed this class and also was able to learn a lot of things.

I really learned a lot from the class. I think my lecturer motivated me a lot.

In year three, this learning objective was assessed using an instrument more qualitative in nature. In the midterm survey, students were asked to answer the following questions:

1. You have recently started your design project involving work with school teachers to design equipment that can be used in math and science instruction. How relevant do you think the project you have begun is to your training as an engineer? What makes it relevant (irrelevant)?
2. How has your experience with the project so far changed your ideas about community service? If it has changed your ideas, explain how. If it has not changed your ideas, why not?

In the postservice survey, students were asked to answer the following questions:

1. You have recently completed your design project involving work with school teachers to design equipment that can be used in math and science instruction. How relevant do you think the project you have completed is to your training as an engineer? What made it relevant (irrelevant)?
2. How has your experience with the project changed your ideas about community service? If it has changed your ideas, explain how. If it has not changed your ideas, why not?

In the midterm survey, only 10 students returned the survey and nine of the 10 mentioned that the project modeled the processes a professional engineer would engage in. The student who did not mention the design process talked instead about the project as a potential builder of his or her competence in taking on future projects. Only one of the 10 students in the preservice survey stated the project had already changed his or her view of community service because he or she was learning from social activities to become a good and reliable engineer.

All 13 students participated in the postservice survey, and their responses included the following:

Relevance of Project: All students mentioned that the project gave them an experience that helped them learn about design in practice. Some of the comments were:

Doing an actual project better prepares me for the future.

I learned about working with clients.

The project shows how important team effort is in engineering.

I used many engineering principles to complete the assignment.

If I do my best, I can have fun too.

The project enhanced team skills and introduced us to specifications and other design-related criteria.

Community Service: Eight of the 13 students reported they already felt and remained positive about community service, and three students actually reported they were now more positive about community service. One student stated, however, that he or she would only offer such service if required. One student did not respond to this question. Therefore, at the very least, students' positive views of community service were maintained and maybe even strengthened by the time the course ended. Some of the student comments included:

It has changed me a lot because I believe each individual can be productive in society if he wants.

I used to not believe in community service, but now I believe I should do more. Universities need to do more too.

My ideas about community service are basically the same. I wouldn't do it unless I had to. Although when I have done it, I feel better about myself.

By helping others, you receive gratification.

Community service is better than I previously thought.

On the other hand, one student stated, "I don't consider what we're doing to be community service, since we're doing most of the work in the library and such facilities."

Conclusion and Recommendations

Overall, the service-learning projects in ME 125 provided a positive learning environment for a majority of participating students, allowing them to achieve the course's learning objectives and to meet most of their teacher-clients' educational needs. Although the quantitative results of student assessment are mixed, the qualitative results support the conclusion that the course's learning objectives have indeed been achieved. Despite a complaint by one student, the majority of the student comments regarding the service-learning projects and the course were very positive and several students even offered constructive suggestions; for example, "Change the project to high school students so we could delve deeper into more complex math concepts" and "Make the course a writing course."

Recommendations to engineering faculty members interested in integrating service-learning into a course of this kind are:

• Meet with teacher-partners prior to the actual course to discuss the service-learning projects and to ensure that the teachers' classroom needs really do accommodate the course's learning objectives. Sometimes the needs of the teacher-partner can be better met by a technician than an engineer.

• Begin the service-learning project as early as possible, and provide guidance to the students through case studies that illustrate each step of the engineering design process.

• At the start of the project, inform both the students and their community partners that scheduling can present hurdles, and overcoming them will require effort, mindfulness, creativity, and persistency on everyone's part.

• Be prepared for student challenges. In one instance, a student in ME 125 was very vocal, clever, and persistent in his challenge. At first, he based it on his objection to experiential learning for middle school students, stating that middle school students are not developmentally ready for such a learning experience. I explained to him that he and his team could design a solution to meet their teacher-clients' needs using learning methods more compatible with his belief system. This did not end his challenge, because he then organized and filed a complaint with the department chair, stating that the course is not related to mechanical engineering. (As it turned out, this student was a self-proclaimed disciple of Ayn Rand.[3])

• Use resources already available to develop course materials and assessment tools. This is especially important with regard to those topics that engineering faculty traditionally have less experience with, such as teaching teamwork.

Notes

1. For more information, contact Johnson at <bjohnson@usamail.usouthal.edu>; Newman at <jenewman@usamail.usouthal.edu>; and Van Haneghan at <jhaneghan@usamail.usouthal.edu>.

2. Learn and Serve America: Higher Education. Grant #95LHB00024.

3. The Ayn Rand Institute website <http://www.aynrand.org/medialunk/>. Essays and opinions expressed by the Ayn Rand Institute oppose community service (including community service and service-learning in higher education) on moral grounds, stating "it is the opposing morality, 'that of selfishness,' that enables man to achieve his own happiness." One example is "Public Service and Private Misery" by David Harriman, which was published as an editorial in *USA Today* on April 23, 1997.

References

Anwar, S. (1995). "Development of a Collaborative Problem Solving Instructional Model and Its Implementation in Engineering Technology Classes. In *Proceedings of the 1995 Annual Conference of the ASEE, Vol. 2,* pp. 2316-2329.

Accreditation Board for Engineering and Technology. (1998). *Engineering Criteria 2000.* Available on ABET's website at <http://www.abet.org>.

American Society for Engineering Education. (1994). *Engineering Education for a Changing World.* A joint project report of the Engineering Deans Council and the Corporate Roundtable of the ASEE. Available on the ASEE website at <http://www.asee.org>.

Bellamy, L., D.L. Evans, D.E. Linder, B.W. McNeil, and G. Raupp. (1994). "Teams in Engineering Education." National Science Foundation report, grant number USE9156176, Arizona State University, AZ.

Gerbec, D.E., D.N. Skillman, and S. Conrad. (1994). "The Implementation of Design Projects in a Freshman 'Introduction to Engineering' Course." In *Proceedings of the 1994 Annual Conference of ASEE, Vol. II,* pp. 2325-2330.

Hart, D., B. Engerer, and D. Goodman. (1994). "A Coordinated Freshman Engineering Program." In *Proceedings of the 1994 Annual Conference of ASEE, Vol. II,* pp. 2314-2318.

Herzog, H. (1994). "Stimulating Creative Problem Solving in Freshman Orientation: Thirteen Practical Suggestions for Implementing a Successful Course." In *Proceedings of the 1994 Annual Conference of ASEE, Vol.* II, pp. 2309-2313.

Johnson, R.B., E.J. Newman, and Sandy Van Eck. (1996-1997). "USA College of Engineering: Learn & Serve Mobile." Annual report to the Corporation for National Service: Learn & Serve Higher Education Program. Washington, DC: Corporation for National Service.

Kozick, R.J. (1994). "Electrical Engineering Laboratory for First-Year and Non-Engineering Students." In *Proceedings of the 1994 Frontiers In Education Conference*, pp. 63-67.

National Science Foundation. (1996). "Shaping the Future: New Expectations for Undergraduate Education in Science, Mathematics, Engineering, and Technology." NSF report 96-139. Available from the NSF website at <http://www.nsf.gov>.

Service-Learning and Civil and Environmental Engineering: A Department Shows How It Can Be Done

by Peter T. Martin

There have been many definitions of service-learning. Morton and Troppe (1996) define it as

> *a form of experiential education, deeply rooted in cognitive and developmental psychology, pragmatic philosophy, and democratic theory. Informed by a range of intellectual traditions combining organizational development and participative research, service-learning is based on the principle that learning is founded on experience. Community service provides the experiential basis.*

Kendall and Associates (1990) approach it through students' seeing their work in a larger context of issues of social justice and social policy as well as issues of philanthropy and charity. Stanton (1990) stresses the reciprocity of campus and community and of serving and learning. Service-learning is described both as experiential learning and as an expression of values, facilitating, through service to others, community development and empowerment, as well as a reciprocal learning arrangement that determines the purpose, nature, and process of social and educational change.

In the Department of Civil and Environmental Engineering at the University of Utah, service-learning is defined as an academic exercise whereby students are required to reflect on the real-life application of their study. Students engaged in service projects meet genuine needs of the community and the organizations that serve them, combining traditional campus-based methods with community-focused activity.

One of the principal reasons for the prominence of the University of Utah as a service-learning leader is the existence of the Bennion Center, founded in 1987. This unit provides guidance, support, and experience to enable faculty to initiate and develop service-learning ideas. It seeks to identify courses that can accommodate a service component, thereby encouraging the creation of new service-learning classes. The center also plays a "licensing" and quality-assurance role through its review of courses. Each potential service-learning course is evaluated according to a specific set of criteria. Those approved are designated by an "SL" suffix in the university course catalog. Once approved, the initial offering of the new course is supported through the assignment to it of a Bennion Center–funded teaching assistant. Subsequent offerings are supported through faculty and teaching assistant training and objective course assessments. The center, in this way, represents a resource for initiating, nurturing, and developing service-learning programs across the curriculum.

The approach to service-learning in civil and environmental engineering reflects the drive and influence of the Bennion Center. Bonar et al. (1996) have created a special service-learning faculty guide. Wide-ranging in scope, the guide explores service-learning from local, regional, and national perspectives. It provides a lucid rationale for service-learning in higher education and offers detailed practical suggestions for course development. With the help of this material, civil and environmental engineering students acquire a fresh perspective on their roles as citizen-professionals. Fundamental principles are linked to a new social perspective so as to provide them with an enhanced understanding of what it means to become a professional engineer. They acquire a better feel for the way engineers must discharge the rights and responsibilities of their profession. In short, this approach combines multidimensional knowledge with community need to forge three-way partnerships among students, the local community, and the profession.

The remainder of this paper shows how the combination of support from the Bennion Center and the distinctive characteristics of the civil and environmental engineering profession have combined to create a set of core courses. Its purpose is to show how other university departments can embark, step-by-step, on their own programs of bringing service-learning into the curriculum.

Community Needs

One of the challenges of setting up a service-learning course is the identification of an appropriate community need. This translates into the problem of how to find service "customers." Actually, finding such customers has not proved difficult for the Department of Civil and Environmental Engineering. Academics who work in the applied discipline of civil engineering are almost by definition connected to their local communities. Their research and professional activities bring them into regular contact with engineers from city, state, and federal government agencies. They contribute to the political process through research projects, consulting assignments, and interaction with the media. It is clear, therefore, that faculty routinely connected to needs and initiatives associated with their discipline will have little difficulty in identifying projects that support their educational goals while providing assistance to the local community. They are indeed uniquely equipped to bring together the needs of their students, their government colleagues, private practitioners, and their communities.

In the growing metropolitan region of Greater Salt Lake City, the infrastructure demands are plain to see. Traffic problems for commuters, shoppers, and recreationalists are the subject of continuous media coverage. As good citizens, faculty cannot fail to be aware of growing concerns about air quality, the water supply, and the impact of tourists on the wilderness. If, therefore, there is a problem in identifying projects for service-learning classes, the problem rests with the faculty. Happily, no such problem exists at the University of Utah.

For other engineering disciplines, community needs may be less obvious. However, one of the better ways to secure community partners is through the local media. Most universities have public relations specialists who are required to promote the institution's image. Faculty can prepare carefully crafted press releases and launch other initiatives that provide local exposure for the resources and teaching mission of the department in question. In civil and environmental engineering, for example, the acquisition of a trailer-mounted traffic speed device has enabled the department to serve and to catch the attention of neighborhood communities.

The Courses

The department currently offers five key service-learning courses to civil and environmental engineering majors and has plans to introduce more. Transportation is taught with service-learning components at both undergraduate and graduate levels. An undergraduate course in water engineering comes with a service-learning component, and a technical elective in environmental engineering tackles remediation of landfill groundwater pollution. The undergraduate capstone — a senior design course — is presented in a wholly service-oriented format.

In the two transportation engineering courses (undergraduate and graduate) students model local traffic problems, consult local community groups and transportation officials, and present their findings in written technical reports. They deal with many common traffic problems in both urban and rural settings, such as traffic signal warrants, unwanted commuter traffic scuttling through neighborhood streets, traffic calming, and acceptance of a new light rail system. They are working with several community groups on a rural "Para-Transit" development made possible by sharing limited transportation resources. People from nursing homes, disabled groups, and wheelchair users share vans with the blind. The idea is to share excess capacity and reduce unit costs through the installation of information technology. The students assess each group's route choice and trip behavior and apply operations research techniques to optimize the collective fleet efficiency.

Transportation studies encompasses a wide variety of disciplines. The courses have been designed to provide insight into transportation planning, traffic control, and management techniques. The course objectives include a basic understanding of the principles of traffic flow theory and the development of independent analytical techniques for solving transportation problems. In this context, one important function of the service objective is to help students cultivate a meaningful understanding of the way traffic engineering relates to community issues. Course topics include traffic flow theory, speed flow analysis, statistical representation of traffic data, highway and traffic safety, and the evaluation of transportation alternatives.

In water engineering, students deal with community concerns for such conflicting needs as water supply, pipe construction, and preservation of the local habitat. A 35-acre lake, for instance, provides local flood control and serves as a detention basin. Stressed by new industrial developments, more residential properties, and growing recreational demands, the lake is suffering. Sediment is filling it, and pollution levels are rising. A local wetlands preservation foundation established in 1994 promotes preservation of the lake. Working with the foundation, city officials, and the county, students generate storm hydrographs to model flow conditions for the five watersheds that feed the lake.

The capstone senior design course is set up with a client group and a constituency group. Civil engineering undergraduates have addressed road safety through the design of footbridges and underpasses, and have designed a development plan for the Antelope Island buffalo preserve that improves access to the site while preserving its unique ecological quality. To deal with sewage disposal, students are assessing novel approaches to the complex problem of accommodating an expanding domestic effluent component while treating toxic industrial waste.

In a course on bio-process fundamentals, environmental engineering students investigate how to improve the quality of the groundwater affected by municipal landfills. The groundwater, or "leachate," contains heavy metal and organic contaminants resulting from the interaction of clean groundwater with domestic and industrial waste deposited in landfills. Working with environmental monitoring agencies, the students assess the effectiveness of photo remediation with sunflowers removing heavy metal contaminants. They test bio-absorption techniques by trickling leachate over a simple filter and then pumping it through a column of peat moss-based beads.

These courses serve to introduce the theoretical principles that underpin transportation and environmental engineering. In applying principles of engineering science to real problems, students are required to engage local communities with a need and to identify local concerns. They do this by presenting alternative engineering solutions and listening to the community response. Courses are structured around three stages of community contact. At the outset, students meet the appropriate neighborhood group and listen to their concerns. Midcourse, they present their preliminary findings and actively record the community response. At the end of the course, having refined their designs in response to the midcourse contact, they present their revised findings to the community at a final meeting. They document their designs in report format for government engineers and other professionals, who in turn provide written comment on the student reports.

Thus, the instructor assumes new functions, providing a framework for the course and playing an advisory role while teaching basic engineering in a traditional classroom-style lecture format. Breaking with tradition, students do not tackle textbook examples. Instead, the instructor provides carefully crafted demonstrations and case studies. Students then move directly to the conversion of community needs into engineering problems. Instead of delivering an entire body of knowledge from the lectern, the instructor serves as a catalyst, facilitator, and guide. Students design, prepare presentation materials, and formalize their work in written reports. The instructor's role is to respond to their ability to communicate their designs. Instead of grading with a red pen and an answer sheet, he or she asks questions. Engineering students — who are often reluctant to write — find that their work is critiqued for readability. An academic grading exercise is thereby converted into an exercise that prepares for the effective transmission of information to others. Similarly, presentation skills are honed for a practical purpose: to present ideas to others beyond the campus. In short, the role of the instructor is to enable students to learn design principles, apply them, and then communicate them to their peers, the community and their profession.

Taking a transportation course as an example, we will next examine the nature and design of a typical course.

Course Design

The purpose of the department's transportation courses is to introduce students to the theoretical principles that underlie the field of traffic engineering and to demonstrate how those principles are applied to highways, city streets, and residential roads. The courses address the roles, responsibilities, and characteristics of road users of all ages. When applying traffic flow theories to real problems, students must engage local communities with relevant needs and identify local concerns. After detailed analysis of those needs, they develop a set of alternatives. Next they present their alternative engineering solutions for open discussion with local groups; e.g., neighborhood committees, road safety activists, lay city advisory boards. One student is selected by the class as its liaison officer.

This approach makes it more likely that traffic management projects will secure the local support so essential for their ultimate implementation. But besides addressing real traffic problems in real communities, projects must also meet several other conditions. They must relate to the practical application of theories formally introduced in class, and they must enable students to follow the way in which theoretical principles make it possible for the professional engineer to help communities resolve transportation problems.

Course time is split in four ways: some 30 percent is allocated to preparation, attendance, and review of community meetings; 40 percent is allocated to formal lectures; and 20 percent is spent on discussion and reflection. The remaining 10 percent is allocated to classroom discussion with professional engineers.

What follows is a sample of some of the community concerns addressed by students from a service-learning class. Note that the community concern or need is first identified and then translated into specific technical objectives. Identification of need is the first part of the exercise and is managed by the students. Lacking technical expertise, the community often articulates needs that are initially too ambitious. Students must then point out that they are engaged in a single class project, not a community needs degree program! With guidance from the instructor and close consultation with the community, the needs first articulated are eventually refined into meaningful questions that are relevant to the course material and of a scope that renders them attainable in the time available. Hence, it is at this early stage that the expectations of both the community and the students are aligned.

Case Study: Community Needs

A traffic action group concerned with growing congestion worked with a class to define the following objectives:

• Residents living above and below one of the main arterial routes into Salt Lake City have difficulty leaving and entering their neighborhoods safely through their access road. Are traffic signals warranted at the intersection of the access road and the arterial? What other solutions are possible? *Student technical objectives:* How can the safety of this intersection be improved? What is the full range of possible turning maneuvers? Can arterial traffic be slowed down in the vicinity of the access road intersection?

• Residents accessing the arterial and primary distributor intersection (main road, side road intersection) endure long delays. They often wait through several signal cycles for an opportunity to turn onto or cross the arterial in order to leave their neighborhood. *Student technical objectives:* Can the signal timings be adjusted to help neighborhood traffic without adversely lengthening arterial delays? Is a protected left turn warranted? Is there room for a right-turn-only lane?

- Morning commuters using the main arterial seem to be rerouting through the residential neighborhood to avoid the morning commute congestion. Traffic signs installed to inhibit the practice seem to be ineffective. *Student technical objectives:* Determine the rate of compliance with the existing signs. Quantify proportion of commuter traffic diverting through neighborhood streets. Determine whether more onerous traffic control measures are necessary.
- Morning and evening traffic volumes on the main arterial appear to exceed the design capacity for the roadway as built. With increasing traffic loads expected, how can the capacity be increased? *Student technical objectives:* Determine the existing capacity of the roadway. Determine how the capacity of the arterial can be increased and at what cost.

The initial public perceptions of the problem were of increasing traffic volume and speed. The community attitude was one of bewilderment at engineering technology and analytical methods, coupled with cynicism about the entire process. This initial attitude can be summed up as "We are bewildered by your fancy technology, but we know all the answers (although we're not sure of the questions)."

At first, the students were seen as stooges for a city Transportation Department that had simply abrogated its responsibility. However, many of the skeptics were won over when they saw that the students were motivated only by a desire to learn and to earn a grade. They saw that there was "no other, hidden agenda." Furthermore, when the students presented their designs, they demonstrated their ownership of those designs. Designs relied in part on official data but also on the students' direct field investigations. As the students learned the importance of evaluating the quality and completeness of information, the community recognized that what was being made available to them were free designs and analyses reflecting an honest, fresh, direct approach to the problems at hand. They recognized that they were now participating in an informed debate.

Thus, the students learned that the public can be both suspicious and forgiving. They also learned that, as engineers, they will be held accountable for the breadth and consistency of their design assumptions. They learned that their new-found technical expertise is of genuine value to the community — but that one of their professional challenges would be bridging the gap between the engineer's mind and the activist's heart.

Case Study: Grading

With such an approach to learning, grading must have several components. The community contributes through evaluating the responsiveness of the students to their concerns. The professionals assess the quality of the documentation. Peer group assessment allows students to evaluate the effectiveness of other class members. Finally, the instructor provides an overall assessment based on his or her observations of student learning as demonstrated in discussion, journals, presentations, and design production. The instructor retains a component of the grade assessment but delegates the majority to the other participants. This is in accord with his or her providing a framework for the course and playing an advisory role.

The students must be assessed for the purpose of grading, but it is also necessary that the service provided be assessed. It is only through striving to measure the value of the class effort to the community that the students come to recognize the value and meaning of the service. Furthermore, such a service assessment provides the instructor with valuable insight on how to modify the service-learning dimension of the course for the benefit of future classes and community groups. The community itself, therefore, contributes to the assessment of the student service effort. Typical in this regard is the survey (opposite) of members of a small but active neighborhood community group concerned with traffic problems.

Once collected, such a community assessment is discussed by the class. Here, students explore in depth the nature of the relationship between the professional engineer and his or her constituents. Having worked with real people from real communities who have evaluated their efforts, the class engages in discussions that have a relevance and a penetration rarely encountered in traditional-style student projects. Furthermore, since the instructor will use the community survey findings to modify the next iteration of the course, he or she also facilitates class discussion in a way that allows that discussion to contribute to this topic.

Finally, the learning derived from the service component is also assessed through peer-group evaluation. Each class member reviews the contribution of his or her colleagues. Students are required to take the community survey findings into account in their assessments. (An example of a peer-group evaluation form is reproduced at the end of this paper.)

Educational Needs

Identifying community needs is one challenge. Capturing the special needs of students that service-learning can address is another. Taking transportation engineering as an example, one notes that many aspects of the disci-

Community Response to Student Project

1. Were the students receptive to your comments and suggestions?

very open	open	somewhat	limited	not open at all
1	8	8	4	0

2. How well did the students address your concerns?

very well	well	somewhat	not very well	not at all
1	5	4	9	2

3. Were the goals of the design project made clear to you?

very clear	clear	somewhat	unclear	not clear at all
1	10	10	1	0

4. How well did the class balance the concerns of those of you directly influenced by road traffic improvements with the concerns of those people living in the general neighborhood?

very well	well	somewhat	not very well	not at all
3	4	7	3	2

5. How satisfied were you with the depth of analysis performed by the class?

very satisfied	satisfied	somewhat	unsatisfied	not at all
2	7	8	4	0

6. How well did the students enhance your understanding of traffic engineering in your neighborhood?

very well	well	somewhat	not very well	not at all
4	6	6	4	1

7. How clear and understandable were the students' presentations at community meetings?

very clear	clear	somewhat	unclear	not clear at all
3	8	10	0	0

8. How likely are the city authorities to implement the students' proposals?

very strongly	strongly	don't know	probably not	not at all
1	2	8	7	2

9. If the students were to do this type of project again, how would you suggest it be done differently?

10. Any other comments?

pline have not been addressed in the traditional classroom environment. For example, we do not give lectures on how to identify a community need. We do not show how to extract information from the context of a community problem. Instead, we ask our students to solve problems from a predefined set of criteria. We ignore what is most often the most challenging aspect of design, namely, problem formulation.

When faced with a service-learning assignment, students find that having formulated a problem they can identify several alternative approaches. With ownership of those alternatives, they are better able to evaluate the pros and cons of each. Such an evaluation is done under the scrutiny of the client or community. This teaches students something about accountability. It also teaches them about the importance of making, documenting, and substantiating their assumptions. It drives to the very heart of what it means to practice engineering.

Students engaged in service-learning must communicate with various sectors of the public — local government leaders, other engineers, activist groups, and neighborhood residents. Communication skills, like all skills, have to be learned, practiced, and polished. Students learn how to listen as well as how to transmit technical ideas to those with little technical background.

For the most part, civil engineers directly serve the public, rarely working for a private client. Whenever a project is funded through public money, a significant political dimension emerges. The old maxim is worth repeating: Politics is far too important to be left to the politicians. Through service-learning, engineering students learn that the promotion and selection of an infrastructure project has a political dimension from the outset. More important, they learn that as engineers they have a responsibility to contribute to the political process. They learn that engineers who abrogate this component of their professional responsibility diminish their leadership status, reducing their role to simply providing technical support.

In transportation issues, engineering students learn that poor solutions are implemented when engineers ignore the political aspects of their work. They learn that many traffic engineering decisions can be made on political grounds with no technical justification. Students learn about the political power of neighborhood councils, activist groups, and city council members and why these groups sometimes influence decisions more than do city engineers. They learn about citizenship, but not from a class called Citizenship.

Discussion

Civil and environmental engineers address the construction, development, and maintenance of an infrastructure that impacts all of us. The public is often suspicious of the promotion and execution of new projects. This mistrust is sometimes based on a lack of understanding of the issues. The University of Utah offers the community an independent source of guidance and leadership. It serves as a vital bridge between the community and government professionals and their agencies. The students are the builders of this bridge — the university representatives who apply their engineering expertise to real community concerns. They learn that the technical component of their work is engineering design, but also that their technical expertise represents an important community service and that the actual design process should be informed by public opinion. They learn, in a way that can never be taught in a classroom, that they must communicate their skills to the public they serve. In this way, their technical education acquires a new relevance. It also means that they begin to develop new skills. Knowing what they write will be read by more than their professors, the students become more motivated to write. Reluctance fades as relevance of need becomes manifest.

However, faculty also benefit from service-learning. Instructors are invigorated by a process that enables students to learn as never before. For example, in statistical analysis, we have to teach students to distinguish between precision and accuracy, and how to derive a representative sample. We show them how to manipulate data, and they readily apply these computational "tricks." Often, the real meaning of these processes is lost on students focusing exclusively on mechanical computation. When a group of students present traffic statistics to a community group, they learn that they must first understand the relevance of concepts such as confidence limits, survey bias, and the bounds on error. They are motivated to learn because they know they will have to justify and explain their analysis to others. Such motivation is rare in a traditional academic environment. It is rewarding as an instructor to see students delve into ideas on their own initiative.

Finally, the service-learning experience helps engineering students realize that they can develop from being technocrats remote from the communities they serve to being true professionals. Since engineers are trained to focus on solving technical problems with quantitative techniques, their education tends to encourage them to think quantitatively rather than qualitatively. Service-learning adds to their education a qualitative dimension that helps them become more rounded in the way they think.

Conclusion

A service-learning course, within an engineering program, should be established through a series of steps. First, the instructor must identify an appropriate community problem well in advance of the start of the course. This requires that he or she remain open to potential projects at all times. Press releases are a proactive way to solicit ideas. Professional associations should be cultivated to help identify other project possibilities. Second, a series of community meetings should be arranged. The first session can provide a forum for the community to express its need and for students to respond with preliminary methodological suggestions. Here the instructor plays a key role in matching community expectations with student capabilities. Third, the class must be guided as alternative designs are prepared. Fourth, after in-class rehearsals, the students must present their ideas to the community. Fifth, the students should review and incorporate the community response, both informally through classroom discussion and formally by reviewing the community's written project evaluations. The last step is for the students to present, in final report format, their designs to the professionals associated with the project for their assessment and response.

Thus, even before the course begins, the instructor plays a key role in establishing contact with community and professional groups. Meetings must be carefully planned. The concept of service-learning is explained to all involved so that the educational mission influences expectations. With these preparations complete, the instructor goes on to provide in-class guidance on analytical and design methods. He or she offers practical suggestions and support for student alternative designs and represents a reliable link between the outside world and the classroom.

In breaking with many well-established teaching methods, the approach presented here offers much scope for active learning. To be sure, service-learning can entail more work for the instructor as the "Sage on the Stage" becomes the "Guide on the Side." This, in turn, can result in some discomfort, since this new role means that the instructor must relinquish some degree of control. The benefit, however, is a much more rewarding teaching experience, thanks to the enhanced learning that inevitably results.

References

Bonar L., R. Buchanan, I. Fisher, and A. Wechsler. (1996). "Service-Learning in the Curriculum — A Faculty Guide to Course Development." Salt Lake City, UT: Bennion Center, University of Utah.

Kendall, J., and Associates. (1990). *Combining Service and Learning: A Resource Book for Community and Public Service, Vol I.* Raleigh, NC: National Society for Internships and Experiential Education.

Morton, K., and M. Troppe. (1996). "Two Cases of Institutionalizing Service-Learning: How Campus Climate Affects the Change Process." In *From the Margin to the Mainstream: Campus Compact's Project on Integrating Service With Academic Study*, edited by M. Troppe, pp. 3-16. Providence, RI: Campus Compact.

Stanton, T.K. (1990). *Integrating Public Service With Academic Study: The Faculty Role.* Providence, RI: Campus Compact.

Peer-Group Assessment

Rank your first peer using the categories below: "1" best describes your first peer's effort, "5" is the least accurate description:

Name of first peer: ______________________________

no preparation at all	1	2	3	4	5	well-prepared
cooperation	1	2	3	4	5	a real team player
did as little as possible	1	2	3	4	5	large contribution to the project

Rank your second peer using the categories below: "1" best describes your second peer's effort, "5" is the least accurate description:

Name of second peer: ______________________________

no preparation at all	1	2	3	4	5	well-prepared
cooperation	1	2	3	4	5	a real team player
did as little as possible	1	2	3	4	5	large contribution to the project

Rank your nth peer using the categories below: "1" best describes your nth peer's effort, "5" is the least accurate description:

Name of nth peer: ______________________________

no preparation at all	1	2	3	4	5	well-prepared
cooperation	1	2	3	4	5	a real team player
did as little as possible	1	2	3	4	5	large contribution to the project

Cross-Cultural Service-Learning for Responsible Engineering Graduates

by David Vader, Carl A. Erikson, and John W. Eby

Engineering programs everywhere are developing mission statements and outcome assessment plans. Messiah College in Grantham, PA, aims to graduate engineers who are "technically competent and broadly educated, prepared for interdisciplinary work in the global workplace." Moreover, we want to influence our students so that their professional character and conduct would be "consistent with Christian faith commitments." The familiar process of gaining and learning to use new information achieves many of our goals for would-be engineers. But how do we grow beyond merely doing good engineering and learn to do good with our engineering?

This paper first explores the need for responsible engineering. Is technique the principal responsibility of engineers, the material working out of objectives defined and supplied by others? Or are engineers also responsible, in view of our special knowledge, for creating and using technologies in ways that preserve, honor, and advance prevailing social, political, and economic values? The paper then examines the educational objectives of Messiah's engineering program vis-à-vis the college's mission statement and the idea of responsible engineering. It considers the influence of the appropriate technology movement in shaping our vision and the role of service-learning in creating our program. The paper concludes with a case study of an international service-learning project sponsored by Messiah's engineering students.

Responsible Engineering

People outside the profession, and sometimes even engineers themselves, do not understand the nature of engineering work very well. Ron Howard's film about the troubled Apollo 13 moon shot depicts the response of engineers to crises. In one scene, the astronauts' lives are in jeopardy as carbon dioxide accumulates in the disabled spacecraft. Ground crew engineers, working under severe time constraints and using only those supplies available to the astronauts, must make square filtration canisters work in round receptacles. Confined to an office, someone pours the available material resources onto a table. Time passes and disaster seems inevitable, until suddenly the engineers emerge victorious. Amazingly, they have crafted a solution from, among other things, duct tape, plastic bags, and pieces of the flight-plan document. This is engineering at its unambiguous best. When needs, goals, time constraints, and available resources are unambiguous, engineers can solve problems.

Rarely, however, are the scope and boundary of an engineer's work so well defined. In the United States, the Accreditation Board for Engineering and Technology (ABET) describes engineering as devising components, systems, and processes to meet needs. This is the process of applying mathematics and science "to convert resources optimally to meet a stated objective" (ABET 1993: 7). Even this abstract definition of engineering points to *needs, resources,* and *optimums*: how much more subjective is actual engineering practice? Subjective ideals not only motivate an engineer's work; they alter the culture from which those ideals arise. Cultural activities shape our work, and our work is itself shaping cultural activity: planting and harvesting crops, conducting business, starting and raising families, communicating with other human beings (Monsma et al. 1986: 19).

Critics and advocates agree that modern technology is pervasive. Complex equipment, owned by large and interconnected institutions, manufactures even the most basic stuff of modern life: food, clothing, and shelter. Before the Industrial Revolution, artisans in scattered shops used locally produced natural fibers for textiles and clothing. Centralized manufacturers of today's synthetic, petroleum-based fibers depend on international oil fields and distribution systems — pipelines, tankers, roads, and trucks — for raw material. Equipment for weaving these fibers requires low-cost, readily available steel and other refined metals as well as plastics and ceramics. Also needed are reliable sources of water, electric power, and telecommunications. These are the hidden realities behind our convenience culture, on which even something as simple as acquiring an article of clothing is dependent. Disrupting a single strand in this web of technology can affect the basics of everyday life.

Considering these pervasive and complex relationships between technology and turn-of-the-century culture, one wonders that there is so little public discourse on the nature of our commitments to guide the development of technologies. Some of us are technological somnambulists (Winner 1986: 5-10). Engineers have unique opportunities, because of their technical literacy and awareness of developing technology, to foster and contribute to technical discourse. Value questions, however, are often discouraged within the profession and by employers. Engineering addresses empirical issues: Which material will meet technical objectives? What process is most efficient? How can we invent new things (Mitcham and Mackey 1983: 1)? This surprisingly narrow focus on know-how could stem from our approach to technology.

By sharply distinguishing between means and ends, we could almost conclude that technology is value-neutral. According to this view, people make judgments concerning the worth of a technology's end use, but the means to achieve that end is only a "technical" matter. Attaching value to externally defined goals is presumably beyond the control and responsibility of the engineer. Further contributing to the illusion that technology is neutral is a common but simplistic understanding of technology as tool. Once made, according to this argument, tools are used on various occasions for specific purposes that can be either good or evil. This view neglects the ways in which technology provides structure for and reshapes the meaning of human activity (Winner 1986: 5-6). Printing, for example, reshaped religion; automobiles restructured communities; and automation redefined work.

In short, engineering practice and scholarship deal almost exclusively with the issues of forming and using technology (Winner 1986: 6). The stated problem, historically defined and externally supplied, determines the character of most technological thought and activity (Jarvie 1983: 52). Engineers are already good at solving problems; they could do more to help define them.

Mission of Messiah College

Messiah College is a Christian college of the liberal and applied arts and sciences. We are a church-related institution with a vision of positively influencing communities and institutions through our graduates. Our mission is to educate men and women toward maturity of intellect, character, and Christian faith in preparation for lives of service, leadership, and reconciliation in church and society.

The Engineering Department aims to advance the college's mission through its educational objectives and its program. The department's first educational objective is to graduate technically competent engineers valuable to the companies and organizations they serve. Believing that good engineering is more than an engine for the creation of material wealth, Messiah also aims to graduate engineers who are prepared to work with technology beneficially in a particular social, political, and economic setting. A second educational objective is therefore to graduate engineers broadly educated and prepared for interdisciplinary work in the global workplace. We want our graduates to be familiar with contemporary issues and the historical context of those issues.

Finally, our mission argues that engineering is an inherently value-laden activity. Engineers describe their work as the efficient or even optimal use of resources to meet needs. Messiah engineers seek to benefit or positively influence our world. Only from within the framework of moral philosophy is it possible to recognize and agree on needs, benefits, positive influences, and optimal solutions. While many historical and contemporary voices have articulated philosophies and perspectives, Messiah College is committed to Christian understandings and expressions of what is right.[1] Consequently, a third educational objective of the college is to graduate students whose character and conduct are consistent with their Christian faith commitments. Messiah College engineering faculty and staff aim to accomplish their mission through engineering instruction and experiences, an education in the liberal arts tradition, and mentoring relationships with students. These strategies must, of course, ultimately be expressed in specific initiatives and a particular curriculum. "Appropriate engineering" and service-learning are two ideas that have informed Messiah's program.

Appropriate Engineering

Appropriate engineering is a holistic approach to engineering design that incorporates social, political, cultural, environmental, economic, and human empowerment issues, along with technical considerations, as central to the engineering process. Some principles of appropriate engineering derive from British economist E. F. Schumacher's work in the late 1960s and early 1970s on what he called "intermediate technology." Indeed, his concepts helped start an appropriate technology movement worldwide. The phrase "appropriate technology" refers to

> *local, self-help, self-reliant technologies that local people themselves choose, which they can understand, maintain, and repair. They are generally simple, capital saving, labor enhancing, and culturally acceptable. Ecologically, appropriate technologies are environmentally sustainable, as much as possible using renewable energy, and limiting atmospheric, chemical, and solid waste pollution. (Stevens 1991: ix).*

In one sense, "appropriate engineering" is the creation and use of appropriate technologies.

Although many people have come to associate the idea of appropriate technologies exclusively with low or intermediate technologies, developed nations are also composed of "local people" who might simply choose larger-scale, more advanced, and more capital-intensive technologies. Since the mission of Messiah College is service-oriented, we are very pleased that some of our graduates work in the "Second" and "Third Worlds." But many Messiah engineers also work in U.S. corporations. Whether a local setting is developing or industrial, labor- or capital-oriented, appropriate engineering seeks to privilege it. Recognizing technology's potential for good *and* harm, it aims to do more good than harm.

Because appropriate engineering is a distinctive feature of Messiah's

Engineering Department, opportunities to encourage, promote, develop, and implement its principles are pursued with engineering students, the Messiah College community, and the worldwide community. Appropriate engineering provides a broad and interdisciplinary view of the engineering design process and profession. It fosters an ethical and service-oriented mind-set that informs more typical technical and commercial concerns. Three general ways in which we strive to accomplish this distinctive vision are by:

1. Providing cross-cultural learning and service opportunities for students and faculty through an elective course on Appropriate Engineering, projects in courses such as Introduction to Engineering and Senior Project, and service-learning teams. Student-faculty project teams do design work throughout the academic year. Implementation teams complete projects on-site over the summer and during our January term.

2. Addressing nontechnical issues in engineering practice. We work with other academic departments on mutual projects and ideas. Ethics case studies help us identify and address nontechnical issues in class.

3. Fostering a service ethic among engineering graduates and within our profession. On-campus student clubs such as Habitat for Humanity and Earthkeepers assist in this effort. We make appropriate engineering presentations to alumni, professional society meetings, churches, and para-church organizations. We also cooperate on special projects with worldwide agencies such as the Society for International Ministries and the Mennonite Central Committee.

Service-Learning

The idea of appropriate engineering helps Messiah engineers recognize good engineering; service-learning helps them discover how to do good with engineering. Technology is what philosophers call an "instrumental value" — something valuable not in itself but because it enables one to achieve something else that is intrinsically valuable (Gyekye 1995: 141). Although creating and using technology can, as Samuel Florman (1975) has suggested, provide existential pleasures for an engineer, he or she discovers the value inherent in his or her work only when engineering is practiced as a kind of service. Service-learning, as understood at Messiah, helps facilitate this discovery.

> *Service-learning is a method and philosophy of experiential learning through which participants in community service meet community needs while developing their abilities for critical thinking and group problem solving, their commitment and values and the skills needed for effective citizenship. The core elements of service-learning are (1) service activities*

that help meet community needs that the community finds important and (2) structured educational components that challenge participants to think critically about and learn from their experiences. (Mintz and Liu 1993: 1)

In response to a growing concern about American education, the Carnegie Foundation for the Advancement of Teaching launched a study of what it believed was a foundational issue: the meaning of scholarship. In 1990, Dr. Ernest Boyer, president of the foundation, published a highly influential report, *Scholarship Reconsidered.* Boyer reclaimed as common ground that broad field of activities the academy has too frequently divided into antagonistic polarities: the work we refer to as teaching, research, and professional service. He did this by recognizing that scholarship as a whole can take four appropriate forms — the scholarship of discovery; the scholarship of integration; the scholarship of application; and the scholarship of teaching. The report also emphasized the connections among the disciplines and between the disciplines and general education. Relatedly, it privileged what historically had been a central concern of the academy but neglected in recent years — the application of knowledge in responsible ways to consequential societal problems through service. "Service is routinely praised," Boyer pointed out, "but accorded little attention — even in programs where it is most appropriate" (1990: 22).

Boyer noted that less than a century ago the words *reality, practicality,* and *service* were used by the nation's most distinguished academic leaders to describe higher education's mission. He cited Woodrow Wilson's remark, several years prior to his becoming president of Princeton University, that "It is not learning but the spirit of service that will give a college a place in the annals of the nation" (Boyer 1994: A48). Then, toward the end of his life, Boyer articulated his vision of what he called the "New American College" — an institution that "celebrates teaching and selectively supports research, while also taking special pride in its capacity to connect thought to action, theory to practice" (1994: A48).

Empirical studies have shown that participation in community service leads to personal, moral, and civic development. One controlled experiment showed that students who participated in a service-learning program demonstrated an increased sense of civic responsibility, an increase in international understanding, and a decrease in racial prejudice (Myers-Lipton 1994). In another study, undergraduate ethics students involved in community service as part of a course scored higher on a test of moral reasoning than did students not involved. By the end of the class, 51 percent of the experimental group used principled moral reasoning, while only 13 percent of the control group did so. The service-learning students also participated more in class discussions and showed increased sensitivity to social issues and increased understanding of persons different from themselves (Boss

1994). Other studies have indicated that participation in service-learning increases students' self-confidence, self-reliance, sense of self-worth, tolerance, and leadership skills, thus helping them become responsible citizens, develop career competencies, and experience a sense of self-empowerment (Cohen and Sovet 1989; Coles 1993; Conrad and Hedin 1990; Weaver and Martin 1989).

Cross-Cultural Engineering

There are particular reasons for students to be required to cross social, economic, and cultural boundaries in service-learning. Messiah College encourages every engineering graduate to embrace the ideas of responsible and appropriate engineering. Immersed in our own culture, however, we are often unaware of the social, economic, political, and environmental overtones of engineering practice. Working in situations significantly different from their own will give students an opportunity to develop skills of cross-cultural understanding and to reflect on their experience and culture from the vantage point of another. These experiences will also enable them to identify and relate to the other in our culture.

Messiah is experimenting with cross-cultural service-learning projects as a means of influencing graduates toward a more responsible engineering practice. These projects thus seek to

- Create interdisciplinary learning and service opportunities for Messiah students and faculty;
- Develop new ways of integrating faith and practice;
- Foster a service ethic among Messiah students and faculty;
- Witness the relevance of faith to practice by dissemination via academic, professional, and other public forums;
- Meet physical and spiritual needs through culturally appropriate solutions and Christian testimony.

Service-Learning in West Africa

During January 1996, two engineering students and three college staff[2] visited Society for International Ministries (SIM) missions in West Africa to identify ways of working with SIM to create service and learning opportunities for Messiah students. Following this investigative trip, SIM invited a student-led design team to develop a photovoltaic electric power plant for a medical clinic in the village of Mahadaga, Burkina Faso.

Burkina Faso in West Africa is a landlocked area of the Sahel, about the size of Colorado. The region is prone to drought and famine. Subsistence agriculture dominates the economy, which is also supported by agricultural processing, light manufacturing, textiles, and uranium mining. Annual per capita income in 1992 was $290. Anecdotal reports indicate that this might have doubled by 1998. Infant mortality is 123 per 1,000 births and life expectancy is 48 years. There is one physician in Burkina Faso for every 27,000 people, compared with one for every 400 to 600 Americans. Nearly 50 percent of the Burkinabe population is under 15, while only 4 percent are over 65 (Population Reference Bureau 1994). Burkina Faso is one of the poorest countries in the world.

Electric power needs in Mahadaga are modest by American standards, but provide pumping for drinkable water and lighting for the one clinic. The clinic staff, predominately Africans, assisted by four expatriate women, provide basic health care in the region. Obstetric care is a particularly important service of the clinic. More than 100 difficult births take place at the clinic every month, while many more babies are delivered in local villages. Infant mortality at the clinic is less than 1 percent, whereas the national average is about 12 percent. For many years a diesel generator has been used to fill a water tower and provide electric lighting between 6 and 9 pm. (A few residences in the city are equipped with a single photovoltaic panel and battery storage for lighting after 9 pm.) Deliveries and minor surgery after 9 pm have been conducted with the assistance of flashlights. Fuel is expensive and shortages are common. This, plus the increasing cost and frequency of repairs, motivated the clinic staff to seek alternatives to the generator.

We chose the Mahadaga solar project as our first cross-cultural service-learning activity precisely because its technical requirements were interesting but straightforward. Project management, working on teams, funding, systems testing, and installation were additional challenges that students face infrequently in the classroom — or only in contrived form. Working for a real client, SIM in this case, provided many students with their first genuine opportunity to fail. Although 90 percent earn an A in many courses; our system would either work or it would not. Students raised money to pay for travel expenses, and a donor to SIM provided funds for the cost of the solar panels, batteries, and wiring. Other factors such as international and intercultural communication, shipping, customs, and travel logistics made our activity a very robust learning opportunity indeed.

In the spring of 1996, faculty adviser Dr. David Vader helped Messiah students organize their engineering design team under the direction of three student leaders. Two senior engineering students were appointed mechanical and electrical design leaders. A sophomore was the administrative leader. As many as 17 other students, spanning freshman through senior years and making diverse contributions, were organized under these leaders. The students recognized that a photovoltaic power plant was the customer's proposed solution to the problem of unreliable and costly electric power. They determined, however, that solar power was in fact a more appropriate technology. Fuel and maintenance for generators are scarce in the region, whereas sunlight is abundant. The students chose multilayer thin-film collector technology with polycarbonate covers instead of more efficient polycrystalline or single-crystal photovoltaics, because their choice was more cost-effective and resistant to vandalism. The team also determined that replacing an existing AC well pump with a DC pump would reduce capital and operating costs while eliminating the inefficiency of inverting the power source. Students worked closely with the clinic staff to plan, direct, and implement the project.

After 14 months of learning and system design, we submitted our system proposal to SIM and formed an implementation team to install it in Mahadaga. Only two members of the design team served on the implementation team. The new team consisted of seven students and one alumnus, our mechanical engineering technician, an engineer from the Harrisburg, PA, area, and the faculty adviser. We prepared for intercultural learning by reading and discussing selected fiction and nonfiction on the region and culture. The team also attended lectures provided by Messiah faculty, SIM staff, and local people in Burkina Faso. Each student kept two composition book journals, one for personal reflections and the other for technical record keeping. Four students chose to write a paper focused on a theme, an insight, or a problem coming out of their cross-cultural experience. The implementation team worked for 10 months to take the design from paper to reality. In January 1998 the team traveled to Mahadaga, Burkina Faso, and installed the system.

Students reported on the project on campus, to nearly 300 supporters and interested individuals through a newsletter, to the South Central Pennsylvania Chapter of the American Society of Materials, and to the Pennsylvania Society of Professional Engineers. They hope to encourage other engineers to use their skills in similar service work.

Conclusion

The Mahadaga solar project was both successful and a predictor of the many additional requirements for the long-term success of this initiative. SIM's Alan Dixon reported that "the solar plant is working great. Francoise told me the other day that it is 'merveilleux,' which is about as good as things get in Mahadaga." A baby was delivered and minor surgery performed the very night the system became operational. Just 24 hours earlier clinic staff would have worked by flashlight.

The system was, however, a full week late in coming online. The students' failure to become sufficiently motivated early in their work resulted in delays in the arrival of solar panels and batteries in Mahadaga. We completed the project only by leaving four of our members behind for an extra week. Because parts were shipped only weeks before they were needed in Africa, SIM staff had little time to negotiate with Burkina Faso customs officials, who extracted a $5,000 import tax on our solar panels, half their value. Inadequate testing resulted in our lacking a relay switch for the low-voltage disconnect[3], and although we sent the part later, we suspect the batteries were damaged. Lightning strikes have destroyed several sets of fuses.

These results have been instructional for staff and students. Future projects will require more deliberate instruction in project management, working in teams, and systems testing. We are still uncertain how to teach professionalism and the willpower to adhere to self-imposed work schedules. Since the overall SIM project is constantly never more than a few semesters away from graduating its leaders, a priority assignment for them must be the mentoring of their replacements. Furthermore, although some members of the implementation team have moved on to other things, others continue to work with our friends in Mahadaga to maintain our system. Because Africa is home to many technology projects that failed for lack of resources and the know-how to sustain them, we are proposing a long-term relationship with SIM in Burkina Faso to ensure that our work continues to benefit our "customers." Two students spent the summer of 1999 in Mahadaga installing improved lightning protection, repairing the inverter, investigating reports of low battery capacity, and completing advance work for the next project. We also provided stipends to two students who formed, together with the project advisers, a student-faculty design team. The team worked on campus over the summer to continue design work for a new project.

Our vision and organization have now expanded to include nearly 30 students representing engineering, nursing, business, communication, and other academic departments. New service-learning activities of interdisciplinary teams will help disabled people in Mahadaga gain self-sufficiency and independence.

While our first implementation team was in Mahadaga, a nurse-practitioner working with people disabled by polio and other causes asked the students for assistance. We are now expanding a small farming operation run by disabled children into a self-sustaining agricultural microenterprise. Business students will help develop marketing and business plans. Engineering students are researching and designing human-powered pumps appropriate to that situation to draw water for irrigation. A particular challenge is to develop a pump that can be operated by persons who do not have strength in their lower body. The team is developing several designs — each using a different muscle group — thus allowing pumpers to do physical therapy while pumping water. Disabled persons in Mahadaga, where there are no locally owned motorized vehicles, also need to gain mobility. Some use a hand-powered tricycle, but this device, though functional, is prone to mechanical failure, and repairs are difficult to make. What is needed is a simple, inexpensive, easily repairable hand-powered tricycle that can be manufactured locally. We hope that this, too, can be developed into a self-supporting microenterprise.

Ernest Boyer, alumnus of Messiah College and late president of the Carnegie Foundation for the Advancement of Teaching, once said that the tragedy of life is not death, it is to die with commitments undefined, with convictions undeclared, and with service opportunities unfulfilled. Messiah College professors, staff, and students believe that international service-learning experiences can challenge us to define commitments, declare convictions, and fulfill service opportunities. We have reported here on significant progress toward the creation of a program capable of offering these opportunities to interested persons in our community. Future work must include a longitudinal study to discover how the program has affected the attitudes and actions of participants.

Notes

1. Monsma et al. suggest these normative principles as a guide for responsible engineering: cultural appropriateness, access to information, social communication, stewardship, justice, caring, and trust.

2. Members of this team included Dr. David Vader, chair of the Engineering Department, Dr. John Eby, director of the Agape Center for Service and Learning, and Cindy Blount, director of student outreach.

3. That we were only missing one minor component was actually a positive result. We carried every tool and part, down to the last scrap of wire, to the installation site. The nearest commercial center was 300 kilometers distant.

References

Accreditation Board for Engineering and Technology. (1993). *Criteria for Accrediting Programs in Engineering in the United States.* New York, NY: Engineering Accreditation Commission, ABET.

Boss, J. (1994). "The Effect of Community Service Work on the Moral Development of College Students Ethics." *Journal of Moral Education* 23(2): 183-198.

Boyer, E.L. (1990). *Scholarship Reconsidered: Priorities of the Professoriate.* Princeton, NJ: The Carnegie Foundation for the Advancement of Teaching.

——— . (March 9, 1994). "Creating the New American College." *The Chronicle of Higher Education*, A48.

Cohen, S., and S. Sovet. (1989). "Human Service Education, Experiential Learning and Student Development." *College Student Journal* 23(2): 117-122.

Coles, R. (1993). "Doing and Learning." In *The Call of Service: A Witness to Idealism*, pp. 59-81. New York, NY: Houghton Mifflin.

Conrad, D., and D. Hedin. (1990). "The Impact of Experiential Education on Youth Development." In *Combining Service and Learning: A Resource Book for Community and Public Service, Vol. 1*, edited by J. Kendall and Associates, pp. 119-129. Raleigh, NC: National Society for Internships and Experiential Education.

Florman, Samuel C. (1975). *The Existential Pleasures of Engineering.* New York, NY: St. Martin's Press

Gyekye, Kwame. (1995). "Technology and Culture in a Developing Country." In *Philosophy and Technology*, edited by Roger Fellows, pp. 121-141. Cambridge, England: Cambridge University Press.

Jarvie, I.C. (1983). "The Social Character of Technological Problems." In *Philosophy and Technology Readings in the Philosophical Problems of Technology*, edited by C. Mitcham and R. Mackey, pp. 50-53. New York, NY: The Free Press.

Mintz, S., and G. Liu. (1993). "Service-Learning: An Overview." In *National and Community Service: A Resource Guide*, pp. 1-3. Washington, DC: Corporation for National and Community Service.

Mitcham, Carl, and Robert Mackey. (1983). "Introduction: Technology as a Philosophical Problem." In *Philosophy and Technology Readings in the Philosophical Problems of Technology*, edited by C. Mitcham and R. Mackey, pp. 1-30. New York, NY: The Free Press.

Monsma, Stephen V., et al. (1986). *Responsible Technology: A Christian Perspective.* Grand Rapids, MI: William B. Eerdmans Publishing Co.

Myers-Lipton, S. (1994). "The Effects of Service-Learning on College Students' Attitudes Toward Civic Responsibility, International Understanding and Racial Prejudice." Unpublished PhD thesis, University of Colorado.

Population Reference Bureau. (1994). *World Population Data Sheet: 1994.* Washington, DC: Author.

Stevens, R.W., ed. (1991). *Appropriate Technology: A Focus for the Nineties.* New York, NY: Intermediate Technology Group of North America.

Weaver, H.N., and J. Martin. (1989). "Educational Value of International Experience." In *The Role of Service-Learning in International Education: Proceedings of a Wingspread Conference*, edited by S. Showalter, pp. 59-81. Goshen, IN: Goshen College.

Winner, Langdon. (1986). "Technologies as Forms of Life." In *The Whale and the Reactor: A Search for Limits in an Age of High Technology*, pp. 5-10. Chicago, IL: University of Chicago Press.

Assessment of Environmental Equity: Results of an Engineering Service-Learning Project

by Richard Ciocci

Harrisburg Area Community College (HACC) offers a course called Design for Environment (DFE), Engineering 271. The traditional, primary focus of a course in design-for-the-environment is applying the principles of pollution prevention and sustainable development. DFE courses are designed to teach about air emission, wastewater treatment, hazardous waste handling, and solid waste disposal. The existing DFE course in HACC has been offered twice, and has been made a requirement for the associate's degree in Science in Mechanical Engineering Technology. By design there is no prerequisite, so that students across the college can take it as an elective. All team projects in the course involve engineering analyses with economic benefits as a consideration and social responsibility as a goal of each effort. Examples of projects are: "Disassembly evaluation of a hot water heater," "Solving the use of tires predicament," and "Constructed wetlands for municipal wastewater treatment."

Several factors provided the initial motivation to integrate service-learning into the course in the spring of 1997. Increased awareness of society and the environment has recently become a part of engineering and technology programs, because the environment figures significantly in the global community. Hence, a new direction in engineering education suggests that all engineers and other designers be aware of environmental impacts of products and processes at the earliest stages of product development. With fundamental changes in the design of products and in their associated processes, reduction of negative environmental impact can become significant. Graedel and Allenby (1996) offer their version of a master equation that helps focus efforts on reduction of environmental stresses on the Earth's systems:

Environmental impact is the product of three interrelated factors: (1) population, (2) gross domestic product per person, and (3) degree of environmental impact per unit of gross domestic product. As the first two factors continue to increase well into the next century, the key to reducing environmental impact and moving toward a sustainable society is represented by the third factor: the degree to which technology is available to permit development without causing serious environmental stress and the degree to which such technology is utilized. Although this would seem to be primarily a technological issue, social and economic forces influence the types of technologies that are made available and actually used. What can be done toward environmental improvement is limited in part by sociopolitical considerations, and engineers and designers must be aware of such limits.

Course Design

A goal of the service-learning version of the course is to involve students in identifying actions for environmental improvement by locating a starting base for improving environmental conditions in various Harrisburg communities. Students participating in the service-learning projects ask city and community leaders to identify the current state of affairs; industry personnel for a business perspective on environmental stewardship in general and in reaction to the community-identified concerns; and the Department of Environmental Protection (DEP) for acceptable environmental living standards. Another goal is to have students learn about environmental equity. The two stated learning objectives and their expected outcomes for the course are:

> **Objective #1** — *Students in the course will supplement their study of lecture materials with a service-learning project to identify the degree of environmental equity facing various communities in the city of Harrisburg.*
>
> **Expected Outcome** — *A report identifying positive and negative examples of environmental justice will be shared with city and community leaders.*
>
> **Objective #2** — *As evidence of environmental inequity is identified, the student teams will use state agency standards to evaluate the degree of harm to community members.*
>
> **Expected Outcome** — *The student teams will recommend positive actions based on design-for-the-environment practices that can be taken to rectify any situations identified as detrimental to city residents.*

The students have input into the weighing of the project and how the course will be structured for a grade: They are asked to react and suggest a fair grading system. For spring semester 1997, the final grade for Engineering 271, which is a three-credit semester course, was calculated based on two exams at 25 percent each, six short research assignments worth 15 percent total, and the service-learning project making up the remaining 35 percent.

Implementation

The project has developed in several ways. Early in the semester the class discussed raising awareness in environmental affairs. Specific topics included population, consumption, pollution, and energy. The students did research projects in areas that included environmental equity, sustainability, and eco-feminism; then they contacted individuals representing various sectors of the Harrisburg population. The students hosted a dinner meeting at the college to meet representatives from the community, industry, government, and academic groups and to identify several concerns about the state of the environment in the city. Among the active partner organizations were the Harrisburg Department of Parks and Recreation, Steele Elementary School, Pennsylvania Department of Aging, RE Wright Environmental, Pennsylvania Power and Light, AMP Incorporated, and local chapters of the Audubon Society and the Sierra Club. As a result of the meeting, the students identified the following issues critical to environmental equity in Harrisburg:

(1) the need for a better public transportation system,
(2) the future of the city in terms of regional planning,
(3) the proposed hydroelectric dam project on the Susquehana River, and
(4) the environmental state of Steele Elementary School.

The students formed smaller teams to investigate each of these issues in more detail.

The subproject teams continued interviewing city and community individuals to complete their assessments. Students made trips to various sites in Harrisburg important to their subproject. The class prepared one midterm report that included their observations, conclusions, and recommendations on the stated issues. The written report was distributed to community participants and presented orally at a follow-up meeting.

Assessment Method

The students were asked to identify their individual expectations regarding environmental concerns prior to the project. At the completion of the project, they reevaluated their knowledge of these concerns and compared what they learned with their initial expectations. Also, assessments by city, community, industry, and state officials were solicited through public presentations of the student project's recommendations.

The success of the project was measured by how much the students learned about the issue of environmental equity and the appropriateness of their recommended applications of design-for-the-environment practices to inequitable conditions. In this way, the college would become involved in community affairs, first as an observer, then as an active participant in environmental improvement. A successful project for the college *and* the community would mean both had become more aware of the environmental efforts the other had undertaken.

Results of Student Projects

In their final reports, the teams identified factors that contribute to the quality of life. Tangible factors included air quality, water quality, food supply, energy availability, income per capita, shelter quality, and the visual appeal of the surroundings. The teams also identified less-tangible factors that go beyond traditional engineering concerns. All these, however, ultimately have a direct bearing on environmental equity in Harrisburg (or any other locale). Such factors included social relations, political infrastructure, education, community activity, and general morale as affected by leisure activities. The point of this factor analysis was to show how social and cultural forces impact the overall global environment in such a way that inequities can exist.

Early in the preproject planning, we realized that the students viewed the issue of environmental equity differently than it is presented in some of the literature. Initially, the plan was to assess environmental *inequity* in the Harrisburg area, but after their preliminary research the students argued that the approach should be toward environmental *equity* instead. This subtle shift parallels a more general need for engineers and technologists to be optimistic about environmental improvement. Graedel and Allenby's (1996) formula points to the need for society to utilize its technological resources to its advantage in reducing environmental stresses. In the past, technology has been seen as detrimental, since it has been part of the driving force in our overdeveloped society. That the students recognized the need for optimism in solving environmental problems is not insignificant. Together with their realization that an engineering solution with no social consideration is ineffective, this recognition represented an important lesson learned.

Each of the four subteams made recommendations based on its findings. A recommendation for regional planning was to have a more flexible policy for land use, one that took better account of the qualities of a specific piece of property in the proportioning of that space. A second recommendation based on the parks and recreation input was that Harrisburg should set aside more open space for recreational facilities. The students also suggested the need to use more of the neglected and abandoned sites in the city for conversion to useful land. They recommended land reuse, which is similar to the "brown fields" development initiative that the city has already begun.

The subteam that dealt with Steele Elementary School and its surroundings recognized the need for all city residents to become involved in the operation of the schools. The students recommended supporting Steele School–area residents for school board elections and, at the very least, for more involvement in school operations. Mentoring of students by business and retired persons could help schools that have difficulty meeting demands associated with increasing enrollments. A recommendation for more community involvement in school operations was made as being an extension of the general call for involvement in environmental improvement.

The students who researched the mass transit issue recommended that the city continue its support of mass transit initiatives that are in the planning stages. They supported the Keystone Corridor Project, which is an improved electric train system from Harrisburg to Philadelphia. The team also recommended the addition of park-and-ride lots and high-occupancy lanes to a new Harrisburg beltway. A positive result of such additions could be increased car pooling and fewer automobiles on the area's roadways.

A not-too-popular recommendation came from the hydroelectric project team. The students supported the city's proposal to go forward with the project based on the energy benefits that could be realized. Concerns for wildlife upstream and down were not considered great enough to offset expected benefits.

Conclusion and Recommendations

The service-learning project went well. All of the subproject teams reported observations on the environmental situation in Harrisburg, conclusions from the research efforts made in each area, and recommendations for environmental improvement. The students kept the issue of environmental equity in focus as they worked on the project. Initial reaction to the students' recommendations has been positive, although individuals who have read the students' report or witnessed their presentation did not necessarily agree with each of their recommendations.

Several improvements in the overall project design now suggest themselves. A number of key leaders, such as members of the state Department of Environmental Protection and the Harrisburg School Board, could have been included to expand the scope of the project. Initiatives that are already being considered, such as the light rail system proposed from Harrisburg to Carlisle, should have been included in a more comprehensive study of regional mass transit needs. Economic analyses that have been conducted on the hydroelectric dam proposal could have added validity to the students' recommendations. More time is needed to determine whether the project as conducted actually met the community's needs.

However, the students in this section of Engineering 271 clearly did benefit from the project and their service-learning experience. They experienced an increased awareness of environmental issues, thanks to their interaction with city and community leaders. The lessons they learned from these interviews greatly enhanced the classroom discussions on such topics as planning and wildlife preservation. The inclusion of social and cultural aspects of the environment in the service project was key to understanding the effect of engineering and technology on the overall environment. Students learned about communities and cultures other than their own as they investigated the city for equity issues. This was especially important because none of the 10 students enrolled in the course lived within the city limits. In conducting this assessment, the students participated in a preliminary design-for-the-environment analysis that benefited them in ways that go beyond textbook learning.

Reference

Graedel, T.E., and B.R. Allenby. (1996). *Design for Environment*. Upper Saddle River, NJ: Prentice Hall.

Service-Learning in Engineering at the University of San Diego: Thoughts on First Implementation

by Susan M. Lord

My involvement with service-learning began in April 1998 when I attended a faculty-development luncheon sponsored by the University of San Diego (USD) Office for Community Service-Learning. Dr. Deborah Wiegand of the University of Washington discussed her work with service-learning in chemistry. Having never even heard the term "service-learning," I found the presentation eye-opening. Sometime earlier, several colleagues and I had unsuccessfully tried to establish connections with a local high school. Listening to Dr. Wiegand talk about the need in service-learning to match community needs with academic goals, I suddenly understood why our previous attempts at collaboration had failed — we had not clearly identified the needs of either the college or the high school students.

This sparked my interest, and I attended a curriculum development workshop in June 1998. I was particularly excited to learn about the USD Office for Community Service-Learning and its faculty/student leader collaboration approach. The availability of assistance in locating a community partner made the prospect of incorporating service-learning into a class much more attractive. Throughout the summer, the Office for Community Service-Learning staff and I worked together to develop a placement for my Engr 5-Introduction to Engineering class for the fall of 1998.

I chose Engr 5 for my first service-learning effort for several reasons. At USD, we have a year-long freshman engineering sequence consisting of lectures and a laboratory. In the first semester, Engr 5 students learn about topics such as what engineering is; the engineering design process; and problem-solving and communication skills. A key aspect of learning the design process is having the students complete team projects and make presentations.

In fall 1997, to develop students' oral communication skills, I had them choose an engineering-related topic and give a brief presentation in class. On the whole, these presentations were uninspiring. I felt that one problem with them was the lack of consequences for doing a poor job. Students might receive a low grade, but this grade was only a small part of the course grade and, as such, did not have a large impact. Also, the audience was the other students and the instructor. Students are usually quite reluctant to criticize each other, and it was easy for the presenter to assume knowledge on the part of the audience and the audience to assume that any confusion was due to their own limitations, rather than the presenter's lack of clarity. Service-learning offered the possibility of having a real nontechnical audience who might not be so forgiving if something was unclear. Also the stakes for doing a good job would be higher. I hoped that students who might not care much if they received a mediocre grade would care if they let down a room full of sixth graders.

Furthermore, since most definitions of engineering involve using science or technology to benefit society, participating in service-learning could be a good way to learn about the value of engineering. Then there was the benefit of being able to work with diverse groups of people. Further, service-learning represents an excellent embodiment of the mission and goals of USD, a Roman Catholic institution, to promote students' "intellectual, physical, spiritual, emotional, social, and cultural development." Some of my other motives included a desire both to increase retention — by showing students that engineering can be relevant to their lives — and to appeal to nontraditional students, including women and minorities, who might be especially interested in reaching out to the community.

Course Structure and Logistics

Through the efforts of the Office for Community Service-Learning, we identified middle school — specifically sixth grade — students as good partners. Middle schools need to keep students interested in math and science and motivated to go to college, become technically literate, and possibly pursue careers in engineering. Middle schools also seemed like a good choice because first-year engineering students should feel more knowledgeable than the sixth graders. We chose a school within a few miles of our campus, which has an economically disadvantaged and ethnically diverse student body. Many of these students might not know anyone who has gone to college, so the USD students could serve as college and engineering role models. Once we had chosen a school, we had to identify teachers who would be willing to work with us and who had class times compatible with the USD student schedules. Two suitable teachers agreed to work with us on this project.

As articulated on my syllabus, the project's learning goals for the USD students were:

- To effectively communicate to a real, live nontechnical audience,
- To creatively design and implement an activity,
- To complete a project as a team, and
- To deepen understanding of engineering-related topics.

Students were required to provide the following deliverables:

- Materials for sixth-grade students,
- Team-teaching in Engr 5 a week before going to the middle school,

- Team-teaching in a one-hour science class at the middle school, and
- Project documentation and reflection; i.e., discussion of one's preparation and experience, and reflection on what one learned through this experience.

Student Projects

Peer review revealed that in-class practice presentations were not well prepared and that the presentations needed improvement. Most groups realized that they needed to work harder not to disappoint the sixth graders. By the time those groups went to the middle school, they each had a reasonably well planned activity.

At the beginning of each presentation, the students introduced themselves and explained why they had chosen to major in engineering. Overall, I was disappointed by the students' descriptions of their motivations. Most simply said something like "I became an engineer because I like math and science." I decided I needed to model this assignment better for them; I also recognized that some students were having trouble because they themselves were uncertain whether, in fact, they wanted to continue in engineering.

The table at the end of the chapter summarizes the projects the students did with the sixth graders. Everyone was nervous before the first presentation. However, we left the classroom with a great feeling as sixth graders chanted for specific USD students to come back next time. The middle school students really impressed us when one of them provided a better definition of engineering than did the freshmen.

From this experience, we learned several valuable lessons the hard way: Do not give candy until the end, do not let the middle school students into the hallway, and try to avoid visiting a class when it has a substitute teacher. One group asked the sixth graders what they remembered from two previous groups' visits. I was pleased that they remembered the main ideas related to friction and bridge building. However, when we asked how many of them wanted to become engineers, not many responded affirmatively. But when someone mentioned that engineers make a lot of money, lots of hands went up.

Group 4 (see table) represented a special case because it did its presentation three times. Also, at the end of the presentation, group members talked about what it was like to go to college and how the choices one made in sixth grade could impact one's future. Answering questions from the sixth graders, the USD freshmen learned more about why they themselves had chosen to go to college. I enjoyed seeing their improvement as the students answered the same questions three times. As they did so, they began to realize their potential impact and so found themselves saying things such as, "In college, you go to class because you want to learn, not because you have to." Issues of responsibility, the importance of math and science, and how college provides opportunities permeated the discussion and built upon topics the teacher had raised previously with her class. It is interesting that this teacher in particular was initially hesitant about our visit, but by the time we left, she wanted us to return — a testimonial to the usefulness of the project.

Student Assessment

Students participated in activities that promoted reflection and assessment, including blue books, exams, and surveys. In addition, two students specifically mentioned in final course evaluations that the service-learning project contributed the most to their learning.

Before going to the middle school, students were asked to reflect in their blue books on their concerns, the skills they had acquired that would be useful, and how relevant this project would be for their training as engineers. Most students expressed some concern about not knowing what to expect from the sixth graders. They hoped to use their communication skills, including some we had deliberately worked on in Engr 5 (Seat and Lord 1998: 2). They identified the relevance of this project primarily as helping them improve their communication and teamwork skills.

However, after they had gone to the middle school, most students were impressed and surprised with the intelligence of the sixth graders. Several admitted that they were initially nervous but ended up enjoying working with the sixth graders. Some were pleased that they had taught the students something or that they themselves had discovered new ways to talk about engineering.

On an exam, students were asked to choose from the syllabus the academic learning goals that they felt they had learned the most about during their project. About half of the students felt that they had learned the most about working as a team, and the other half about communicating effectively to a real audience. Here are some examples from student responses.

> *By having a real audience, I was able to understand what I needed to do better and what I did well. This project was very good practice, and I learn best by practicing.*

> *One of the most important things about being an engineer is being able to help other people understand something that they know very little about and that you know a lot about. When I explained the concept of friction to a "real, live" audience, I was very proud that they seemed to grasp it.*

Through the service-learning project I learned how to better work with a team in order to complete a project. Teamwork is essential in electrical engineering or industrial & systems engineering.

I felt that this service project is a great way to teach people to work as a team, because if they don't they will see, just as we did, that the presentation will suffer.

In the students' reflection memos, many of the same themes emerged as in the other evaluation documents: The USD students did not know what to expect from the sixth graders, but they learned about communication and teamwork, enjoyed helping the community, benefited from the in-class practice presentation, and had fun. However, in these memos the students also demonstrated some real insights into themselves, the value of learning, and serving as role models.

When I was up there explaining to the children reasons as to why I chose Engineering, it wasn't until that very moment when I heard myself explaining it to them that I had realized myself why I had chosen to be here studying Electrical Engineering.

Through this experience I was taught a valuable lesson: learning pays off. I now look back on all the years of schooling, the hours of homework, the A's and the F's, and all the knowledge that I gained from school and see how it has paid off in the end. . . . I walked out of the building hoping that maybe just one of those kids was inspired to pursue higher learning. The project inspired me to keep my hard work and [persevere] through one of the rather rougher times of my life.

As could be expected, not all students were initially excited by the idea of service-learning, nor did they understand what it was.

When I first heard the words "Service-Learning Project," I was not very excited to hear about what we would be doing. . . . It wasn't until I learned that we would be sent to a middle school on our own to teach sixth graders about engineering that my attitude changed. The first feeling . . . was excitement because I really like kids. After awhile, though, the realization that these kids would need to get something out of this project other than horseplay brought out a little bit of anxiety in me.

Two students were honest in their reflections on their initial "hatred," or feeling that "it would be nothing more than a big waste of time." However, after doing the project, both students felt it had been worthwhile.

It turned out to be a great experience for me and I think that I learned a lot. One thing that I learned was how the design process can be used for any presentation, and I would highly recommend it to anyone doing any type of project or presentation. I think that this project should be done in future engineering classes.

[After the in-class presentation, I realized] how important this project really was to my engineering education. I, like the rest of my group, realized that the ability to accurately and confidently present what we knew to a group was essential to being a good engineer.

During class time, students filled out a USD evaluation in which they were asked to answer 25 questions on a scale of 1 (very dissatisfied) to 5 (very satisfied). These questions related to service-learning in the classroom, a student's personal response, agency placement, USD support, and impact on the community. Overall, the results were quite positive, with the class average being greater than or equal to 3.58 for each question. Students who chose to provide written comments on these evaluations were generally positive and insightful. Students recognized the need for further improvement in the service-learning component of the class, but expressed their overall satisfaction with the experience.

Regarding service-learning in the classroom, most students again highlighted learning about communication and teamwork.

The service-learning project probably, in terms of education, helped the [sixth-grade] students more than us. Because we already understood the material, we did not learn much. The challenge was in conveying what we know to the sixth graders. In fact, we benefited in other areas, mainly communication.

Several students' personal responses to the experience are illustrated by this comment:

The service-learning is fun, plain and simple. It is a new way to teach material to students in college, communicate those ideas, and help the community in an informal atmosphere.

Not all students agreed. For example, while one student said this was an experience that "I would definitely do again," another thought it was not "a very good use of our time." Students were generally happy with the support they received from USD, particularly the transportation assistance and faculty support. Ten of the students commented that they believed there had been a positive impact on the community. For example, one student remarked:

It is a good educational experience for young students anytime students can come and talk about future schooling. I wish college students would have talked to me about my future when I was in grade school. . . . I feel that what we taught had a great impact on the sixth graders of Montgomery Academy and that the USD students were good role models.

Professor's Experience

This service-learning project involved highs and lows for the students and the instructor. The most rewarding part was definitely working with the middle school students. Their energy, enthusiasm, and intelligence were impressive and contagious. The worst part was the practice sessions in class. The freshmen were more immature than most of the sixth graders. Since I now have some experience working with sixth graders, I hope to provide more guidance to the USD students in selecting appropriate projects.

Another problem was timing. Because arranging the logistics took several weeks, the trips to the middle school occurred in November. By that time, students also had another engineering design project, and many felt overburdened, particularly those who had not begun working on the service-learning project when it was first assigned. By having the service-learning project earlier in the semester — so that it is completed before the second project begins — students could perhaps use what they learn about working in groups in their second project. Also, I was disappointed that the students were not more creative. Much of this was because they did not spend sufficient time on the projects. Next time, I intend to give the students more interim deadlines to ensure that they do not leave matters until the end.

My involvement with service-learning continues to deepen. I plan to incorporate service-learning again in Engr 5, and I look forward to overcoming some of the problems I encountered previously to make this next iteration an even more beneficial experience for my students and their community partners.

Reference

Seat, Elaine, and Susan M. Lord. (November 1998). "Enabling Effective Engineering Teams: A Program for Teaching Interaction Skills." Paper presented at the 1998 Frontiers in Education Conference, Tempe, AZ.

Acknowledgment

I would like to thank Dr. Judy Rauner and the staff of the USD Office for Community Service-Learning and to the students in Engr 5 in fall 1998 for their patience and enthusiasm through this experiment.

USD Student Service-Learning Projects and Corresponding Sixth-Grade Curriculum Standards

Group	6th-Grade Content Standard	Project
1	The student develops an understanding of the relationships among science, technology, and society.	* Teamwork is key to successful project * Marshmallows and toothpicks for pyramids and bridges * Contest: which bridge supports most weight?
2	Friction is a force that resists motion.	* Friction is found in three states of matter * Air resistance as example of friction * Building paper airplanes to turn to right, left or go straight * Contest: Which airplane goes farthest?
3	The student develops an understanding of recurring big ideas and unifying concepts that prove fruitful in explanation, in theory, in observation, and in design.	* Engineering design process steps * Marshmallows and toothpicks for boats * Contest: Which boat supports most weight?
4	Different substances have different solubilities; a substance's solubility is a characteristic of that substance	* Solubility (Kool-Aid vs. salad dressing) * Fire needs oxygen (egg in bottle) * Teamwork (to solve puzzles/ problems) * Questions about college

Appendix

Annotated Bibliography

by Edmund Tsang

Service-learning is relatively new in engineering. Consequently, there is little literature on service-learning and engineering even though there are a lot of publications in the humanities and social science fields. Unfortunately, much of the literature on service-learning and the humanities and social sciences is of little use to engineering faculty members, either because of the differences in the discipline or because the literature contains too much jargon. A short bibliography list is offered here that includes materials on service-learning chosen because they are easy to read, they address the issues of preparing engineering undergraduates for the changing world of the 21st century, or they are inspirational.

Accreditation Board for Engineering and Technology. (1998). *Engineering Criteria 2000*. Available at the ABET website at <http://www.abet.org>.

Engineering Criteria 2000, established by the Accreditation Board for Engineering and Technology (ABET), formalizes the incorporation of "softer" skills to complement the traditional engineering knowledge and skills in preparing graduates for the 21st century. These softer skills were described in early reports on undergraduate engineering education for the 21st century by the American Society for Engineering Education in 1994 and by the National Science Foundation in 1996. The softer skills identified in ABET's Criterion 3, "Program Outcomes and Assessment," include "an ability to function on multidisciplinary teams," "an understanding of professional and ethical responsibility," "an ability to communicate effectively," "the broad education necessary to understand the impact of engineering solutions in a global and societal context," "a recognition of the need for, and an ability to engage in lifelong learning," and "a knowledge of contemporary issues." Service-learning can be an effective pedagogy to meet these program outcomes. Engineering faculty members interested in integrating service-learning into their courses should keep these student performance outcomes in mind as they prepare learning objectives, course materials, and assessment instruments.

American Society for Engineering Education. (1994). *Engineering Education for a Changing World*. A joint project report of the Engineering Deans Council and the Corporate Roundtable of the American Society for Engineering Education (ASEE). Available on the ASEE website at <http://www.asee.org>.

This joint report cites the end of the Cold War, global economy, changing demographics, and information technology as driving forces to reform undergraduate engineering education for the 21st century. The report recommends that engineering colleges accelerate the integration of programs to help engineering undergraduates develop "softer" skills to complement traditional topics in the engineering curriculum. The skills include teamwork; communication skills; leadership; an understanding and appreciation of the diversity of students, faculty, and staff; an appreciation of different cultures and business practices; the understanding that the practice of engineering is now global; and understanding of the societal, economic, and environmental impacts of engineering decisions. Since service-learning provides an ideal environment for engineering students to learn and develop these skills, advocates of service-learning can use this report to appeal to engineering deans for institutional support.

———. (October 1996). "Let Problems Drive the Learning in Your Classroom." *Prism* 6(2): 30-36.

Service-learning is problem-based learning. As such, the roles of the instructor in service-learning are different from those in subject-based learning, which is a traditional instructional strategy in engineering. This essay discusses how problem-based learning is fundamentally different from subject-based, and describes the roles of the instructor in problem-based learning. This essay gives helpful suggestions on guiding students in problem-based learning; faculty members who are interested in integrating service-learning into their courses would find the article useful.

Astin, A.W., and L.J. Sax. (1998). "How Undergraduates Are Affected by Service Participation." *Journal of College Student Development* 39(3): 251-263.

This paper describes the first, large-scale study that demonstrates the positive impact of participation in community service on student learning and development. The study is based on entering first-year students and follow-up data collected from 3,450 students attending 42 institutions of higher learning with a federally funded community service program from 1990 to 1995. The results indicate that, after correcting for individual student characteristics at the time of college entry, including the propensity to engage in service, participating in service during the undergraduate years substantially enhances students' academic development, life skill development, and sense of civic responsibility. Engineering faculty members who are looking for documentation of the benefits of service-learning will find this paper very readable also.

Boyer, E.L. (1990). *Scholarship Reconsidered: Priorities of the Professoriate.* Princeton, NJ: The Carnegie Foundation for the Advancement of Teaching.

Ernest L. Boyer argued in this special report of the Carnegie Foundation that the narrow focus on research as the primary criterion in the faculty reward system is counter to the mission of institutions of higher education. In the preface to this book, Boyer states: "At no time in our history has the need been greater for connecting the work of the academy to the social and environmental challenges beyond the campus." But because scholarship, and consequently the faculty reward system, has been narrowly defined, "the rich diversity and potential of American higher education cannot be fully realized." Boyer proposes four areas of scholarship for university professors: discovery, integration, application, and teaching. He called for "a renewed commitment to service" in institutions of higher learning because, after all, many professors are drawn to "the profession precisely because of their love for teaching or for service — even for making the world a better place." Boyer begins the book by reviewing the roles of university professors through the years and how the definition of scholarship has changed over time. Those faculty members interested in service-learning will find this book useful and inspirational.

Galura, J., ed. (1993). *Praxis II: Service-Learning Resources for University Students, Staff and Faculty.* Ann Arbor, MI: OCSL Press.

This manual identifies the resources available to support faculty, staff, and students participating in service-learning. Engineering faculty members planning a service-learning course will find useful the various forms included in the appendix of this manual to document service-learning. They can either use these forms directly (with attribution to the source) or modify the format to document service-learning to suit a faculty member's special need, including service-learning project activity log and report, and an assessment survey for students about service to the community.

Howard, J., ed. (1993). *Praxis I: A Faculty Casebook on Community Service-Learning.* Ann Arbor, MI: OCSL Press.

This manual describes the 10 elements of best practices in service-learning and provides a step-by-step guide to integrating service-learning into a course. The 10 elements are: (1) Academic credit is for learning, not for service; (2) Do not compromise academic vigor; (3) Set learning goals for students; (4) Establish criteria for the selection of community service placements; (5) Provide educationally sound mechanisms to harvest community learning; (6) Provide supports for students to learn how to harvest community learning; (7) Minimize the distinction between the student's community learning role and classroom learning role; (8) Rethink the faculty instructional role; (9) Be prepared for uncertainty and variation in student learning outcomes; and (10) Maximize the community responsibility orientation of the course.

Jacoby, B., and Associates, eds. (1996). *Service-Learning in Higher Education: Concepts and Practices.* San Francisco, CA: Jossey-Bass.

A primer on service-learning in higher education. The 14 essays are organized into three parts. Part I addresses the "Foundations and Principles of Service-Learning." Part II, "Designing a Spectrum of Service-Learning Experiences," describes various examples of and approaches to service-learning from a wide range of institutions across the United States. The examples are drawn mainly from the humanities and social science disciplines, however, and might prove less useful to engineering faculty members. Part III addresses "Organizational, Administrative, and Policy Issues" of service-learning in higher education.

Kendall, J., and Associates, eds. (1990). *Combining Service and Learning: A Resource Book for Community and Public Service, Vol. I.* Raleigh, NC: National Society for Experiential Education.

This volume consists of more than 50 short essays authored by faculty and administrators on issues related to service-learning in higher education, including profiles of successful service-learning projects. Although none of the essays is related to engineering, this volume can be useful to engineering professors because it contains a history of the service-learning movement and describes some institutional issues and guides to integrating service-learning into a course.

National Science Foundation. (1996). "Shaping the Future: New Expectations for Undergraduate Education in Science, Mathematics, Engineering, and Technology." NSF report 96-139. Available from the NSF website at <http://www.nsf.gov>.

Like the ASEE report discussed above, this 1996 NSF report recommends the incorporation of "softer" skills to complement the traditional topics in preparing graduates of science, mathematics, engineering, and technology (SMET) disciplines for the 21st century. As such, this report provides the arguments for service-learning, and it can be used in addition to the ASEE report by advocates to champion adapting and integrating service-learning into the undergraduate engineering curriculum.

Peters, S., N. Jordan, and G. Lemme. (1999). "Toward a Public Science: Building a New Social Contract Between Science and Society." In *Higher Education Exchange,* edited by Deborah Witte and David W. Brown, pp. 34-47. Dayton, OH: Kettering Foundation.

The Kettering Foundation supports Ernest L. Boyer's call for "a scholarship of engagement" where academic institutions become "more vigorous partner[s] in the search for answers to our most pressing social, civic, economic, and moral problems." (See Boyer above.) The authors in this paper in the Kettering Foundation report argue for the development of "public science," where science (and by extension engineering) is seen as "public work that builds the commonwealth." Public science calls on "scientists to enter into partnerships with citizens from other professions or sectors in work that closely links knowledge creation with public problem solving and policy-making." The authors also state that public science (or "public engineering") might just be catching on in the hard sciences. The paper contains a short description about Jane Lubchenko, a professor of zoology and a recent president of the American Association for the Advancement of Science, on connecting the work of science with the work of citizenship. The paper also contains a brief description of the historical root of public science.

Snow, C.P. (Oct. 6, 1956). "The Two Cultures." *The New Statesman* 52: 413-414.

In meeting the societal needs for the 21st century, the contributions of engineers should not be underestimated, not just because of the special knowledge and skills they bring to the table. C.P. Snow articulated it best in this famous essay, "The Two Cultures," about the "moral health" of scientists, which by inference can be extended to engineers. Snow wrote: "But the greatest enrichment the scientific culture could give us is — though it does not originate like that — a moral one. Among scientists, deep-natured men know, as starkly as any men have known, that the individual human condition is tragic; for all its triumphs and joys, the essence of it is loneliness and the end death. But what they will not admit is that because the individual condition is tragic, therefore the social condition must be tragic, too. Because a man must die, that is no excuse for his dying before his time and after a servile life. The impulse behind the scientists drives them to limit the area of tragedy, to take nothing as tragic that can conceivably lie within men's will. . . . It is that kind of moral health of the scientists which, in the last few years, the rest of us have needed most; and of which, because the two cultures scarcely touch, we have been most deprived." Service-learning is a pedagogy by which engineering professors can cultivate a sense of the moral health of engineers among their students.

Appendix

Contributors to This Volume

Volume Editor

Edmund Tsang
Associate Professor, Mechanical Engineering Department
University of South Alabama
Mobile, AL 36688
Ph: (334) 460-7457
Fax: (334) 460-6549
Email: etsang@jaguar1.usouthal.edu

Authors

Richard Ciocci
Instructor
Harrisburg Area Community College
Harrisburg, PA 17110
Ph: (717) 780-2547
Fax: (717) 231-7670
Email: Rcciocci@vm.hacc.edu

Edward J. Coyle
Professor and Codirector, EPICS (Engineering Projects in Community Service) Center
School of Electrical and Computer Engineering
Purdue University
West Lafayette, IN 47907-1285
Ph: (765) 494-3470
Fax: (765) 494-3358
Email: coyle@purdue.edu

Rand Decker
Professor, Civil & Environmental Engineering Department
University of Utah
160 South Central Campus Drive
Salt Lake City, UT 84112-0561
Ph: (801) 581-3403
Fax: (801) 585-5477
Email: rdecker@eng.utah.edu

John Duffy
Professor, Solar Engineering Program
Mechanical Engineering Department
University of Massachusetts-Lowell
Lowell, MA 01854
Ph: (978) 934-2968
Fax: (978) 934-3048
Email: John_Duffy@uml.edu

John W. Eby
Professor of Sociology and Director of Service-Learning
Agape Center for Service and Learning
Messiah College
Grantham, PA 17027
Ph: (717) 766-2511
Email: jeby@messiah.edu

Gerald S. Eisman
Professor of Computer Science and Director, Office of
Community Service Learning
San Francisco State University
1600 Holloway Avenue
San Francisco, CA 94132
Ph: (415) 338-6846
Fax: (415) 338-0587
Email: geisman@sfsu.edu

Carl A. Erikson, Jr.
Assistant Professor, Engineering Department
Messiah College
Grantham, PA 17027
Ph: (717) 766-2511
Email: erikson@messiah.edu

Leah H. Jamieson
Professor and Codirector, EPICS (Engineering Projects in Community Service) Center
School of Electrical and Computer Engineering
Purdue University
West Lafayette, IN 47907-1285
Ph: (765) 494-3653
Fax: (765) 494-3371
Email: lhj@purdue.edu

Marybeth Lima
Assistant Professor, Department of Biological & Agricultural Engineering
Louisiana State University
Rm. 149 E. B. Doran Building
Baton Rouge, LA 70803-4505
Ph: (225) 388-1061
Fax: (225) 388-3492
Email: mlima@gumbo.bae.lsu.edu

Susan M. Lord
Assistant Professor, Department of Engineering
University of San Diego
5998 Alcala Park, San Diego, CA 92110
Ph: (619) 260-4507
Fax: (619) 260-2303
Email: slord@acusd.edu

C. Dianne Martin
Professor, Department of Electrical Engineering & Computer Science
School of Engineering and Applied Science
The George Washington University
Washington, DC 20052
Email: dmartin@nsf.gov

Peter T. Martin
Associate Professor, Civil & Environmental Engineering Department
University of Utah
160 South Central Campus Drive
Salt Lake City, UT 84112-0561
Ph: (801) 581-7144
Fax: (801) 585-5477
Email: martin@eng.utah.edu

Jennifer Moffat
Coordinator, YWCA Girls, Inc.
708 Martin Luther King Jr. Way
Seattle, WA 98122
Ph: (206) 568-7855
Fax: (206) 568-7851
Email: jenmoffat@hotmail.com

David Vader
Associate Professor and Chair, Engineering Department
Messiah College
Grantham, PA 17027
Ph: (717) 766-2511
Email: dvader@messiah.edu

Series Editor

Edward Zlotkowski is a professor of English and founding director of the Service-Learning Project at Bentley College. He also is senior associate at the American Association for Higher Education.

About AAHE

AAHE's Vision AAHE envisions a higher education enterprise that helps all Americans achieve the deep, lifelong learning they need to grow as individuals, participate in the democratic process, and succeed in a global economy.

AAHE's Mission AAHE is the individual membership organization that promotes the changes higher education must make to ensure its effectiveness in a complex, interconnected world. The association equips individuals and institutions committed to such changes with the knowledge they need to bring them about.

About AAHE's Series on Service-Learning in the Disciplines

Consisting of 18 monographs, the Series goes beyond simple "how to" to provide a rigorous intellectual forum. *Theoretical essays* illuminate issues of general importance to educators interested in using a service-learning pedagogy. *Pedagogical essays* discuss the design, implementation, conceptual content, outcomes, advantages, and disadvantages of specific service-learning programs, courses, and projects. All essays are authored by teacher-scholars in the discipline.

Representative of a wide range of individual interests and approaches, the Series provides substantive discussions supported by research, course models in a rich conceptual context, annotated bibliographies, and program descriptions.

See the order form for the list of disciplines covered in the Series, pricing, and ordering information.

Yes! Send me the following monographs as they are released.

Price per vol. (includes shipping*):	**List** $28.50 ea	**AAHE Member** $24.50 ea	
Bulk prices (multiple copies of the *same* monograph only):	**10-24 copies** $22.50 ea;	**25-99 copies** $21.00 ea;	**100+ copies** $15.00 ea

	Quantity	Price	Subtotal
Complete Series (all 18 vols.)		$405	
Accounting			
Biology			
Communication Studies			
Composition			
Engineering			
Environmental Studies			
History			
Management			
Medical Education			
Nursing			
Peace Studies			
Philosophy			
Political Science			
Psychology			
Sociology			
Spanish			
Teacher Education			
Women's Studies			

Total ______________

Shipping*

Price includes shipping to U.S. destinations via UPS. Call AAHE's Publications Orders Desk at 202/293-6440 x780 if you need information about express and/or foreign delivery.

Payment (F.I.D. #52-0891675)

All orders must be prepaid by check, credit card, or institutional purchase order; except AAHE members may ask to be billed.

- ❑ Please bill me; I am an AAHE member. (Provide member # below)
- ❑ Check payable to AAHE.
- ❑ Institutional Purchase Order/Number: #______________________.
- ❑ VISA ❑ MasterCard ❑ AmEx

Cardholder's Name (please print)

Cardholder's Signature

Card Number   Exp. Date

Bill This Order To (if "Ship To" address is different, please provide on an attached sheet):

Name   AAHE Member # _ _ _ _ _ _ _ _

Address

City   State   Zip

Phone/Email   Fax

Mail/Fax this order to: AAHE Publications, PO Box 98168, Washington, DC 20090-8168; fax 202/293-0073; www.aahe.org. Visit AAHE's website to read excerpts from other volumes in the Series. Need help with your order? Call 202/293-6440 x780.